★ MUSIC ★ FOR ★ YOUNG

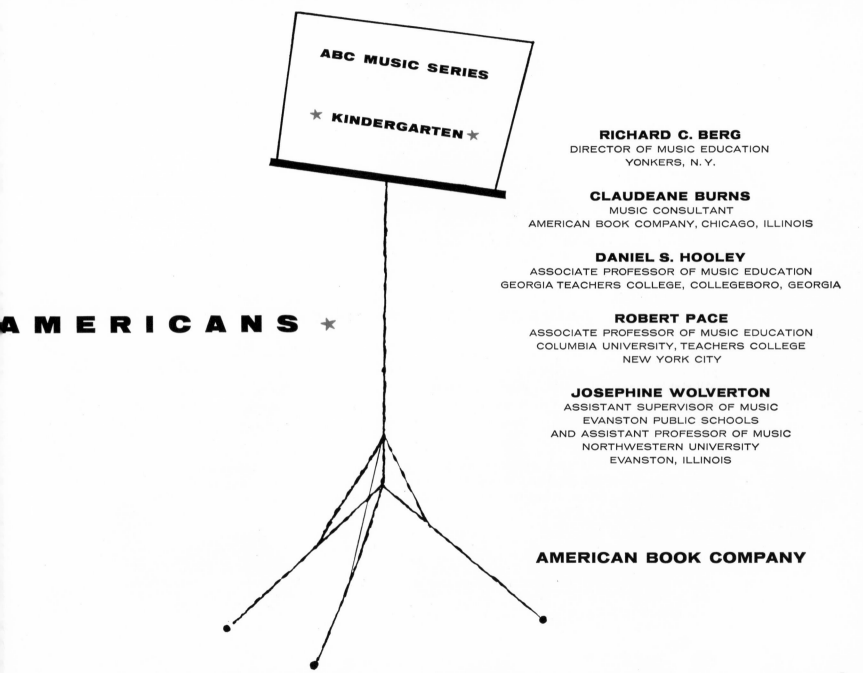

ABC MUSIC SERIES

★ KINDERGARTEN ★

AMERICANS ★

RICHARD C. BERG
DIRECTOR OF MUSIC EDUCATION
YONKERS, N. Y.

CLAUDEANE BURNS
MUSIC CONSULTANT
AMERICAN BOOK COMPANY, CHICAGO, ILLINOIS

DANIEL S. HOOLEY
ASSOCIATE PROFESSOR OF MUSIC EDUCATION
GEORGIA TEACHERS COLLEGE, COLLEGEBORO, GEORGIA

ROBERT PACE
ASSOCIATE PROFESSOR OF MUSIC EDUCATION
COLUMBIA UNIVERSITY, TEACHERS COLLEGE
NEW YORK CITY

JOSEPHINE WOLVERTON
ASSISTANT SUPERVISOR OF MUSIC
EVANSTON PUBLIC SCHOOLS
AND ASSISTANT PROFESSOR OF MUSIC
NORTHWESTERN UNIVERSITY
EVANSTON, ILLINOIS

AMERICAN BOOK COMPANY

©

CONTENTS

Music Gets Inside Me

Words and Music by Daniel Hooley

WITH A SWING

1. When mu-sic gets in - to my feet, When mu-sic gets in - to my feet,

When mu-sic gets in - to my feet, I go a danc-ing down the street!

And I dance like this and I dance like this, I dance and dance and dance.

2. When music gets into my knees, (3 times)
   I shake them just the way I please,
   And I dance like this and I dance like this,
   I dance and dance and dance.

3. When music gets into my hips, (3 times)
   I bounce around in flops and flips,
   And I dance like this and I dance like this,
   I dance and dance and dance.

4. When music gets into my arms, (3 times)
   I get them caught in music's charms,
   And I dance like this and I dance like this,
   I dance and dance and dance.

5. When music gets into my heart, (3 times)
   I try to let a glad song start,
   And I sing like this and I sing like this,
   I sing and sing and sing.

The drawing of a disc 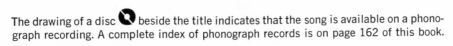 beside the title indicates that the song is available on a phonograph recording. A complete index of phonograph records is on page 162 of this book.

1

Together

Words by Ellen Hertzler   Music by Robert Pace

LOUD-SOFT   FAST-SLOW

2. Together, together
We sing a song ev'ry day;
Together, together
We share our work and play.

3. Together, together
We read a story each day;
Together, together
We share our work and play.

Let the children make up stanzas and suggest changes of tempo and dynamics to suit the mood of each stanza. For instance, a stanza built on "We rest a little while" would be sung slowly and softly.

The autoharp chords are for the 12-bar harp. In this book, slight departures from the harmonies in the piano score have been necessary to conform with the limitations of this instrument.

HAPPILY

1. To - geth - er, to - geth - er, to - geth - er ev - 'ry day; ___

To - geth - er, to - geth - er We share our work and play. ___

The School Bus

Words and Music by Richard C. Berg

STEADILY

1. Oh, the driv-er blows the school-bus horn With a honk and a toot-dee - ay,

And the peo-ple all stop as we roll on by On our way to school each day.

2. Oh, the driver blows the school-bus horn
With a honk and a toot-dee-ay,
And the people all look as we roll on by
On our way from school each day.

Add such stanzas as: And the people all
nod, etc.; And the people all wave, etc. Vary
the tempo by having the school bus go slowly,
then rather fast on succeeding stanzas.

Six Little Apples

Adapted Rhyme   Music by J. W. Elliott

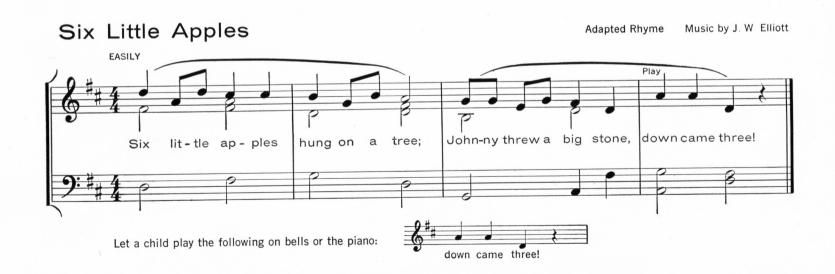

EASILY

Six lit-tle ap-ples hung on a tree; John-ny threw a big stone, down came three!

Let a child play the following on bells or the piano:

down came three!

3

Building Blocks

Words by Mary Francis　　Music by Daniel Hooley

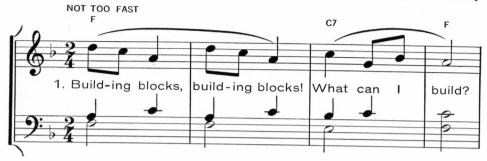

NOT TOO FAST

1. Build-ing blocks, build-ing blocks! What can I build?

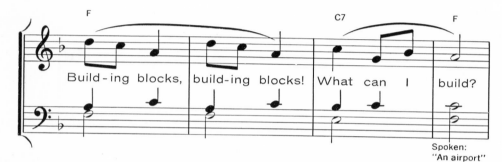

Build-ing blocks, build-ing blocks! What can I build?

Spoken:
"An airport"

I will build an air - port, an air - port, an air - port,

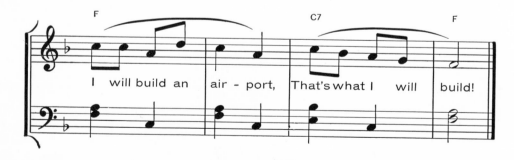

I will build an air - port, That's what I will build!

Add stanzas to this song suitable to your neighborhood: a new house, a schoolhouse, a supermarket, or the like.

4

Building-Block Garage

Words and Music by Richard C. Berg

I will take my build-ing blocks and build my own ga - rage;

Au-to-mo-biles and my toy trucks can park in my ga - rage.

New Clothes

Words by Josephine Wolverton   Old Tune

WITH SWINGING MOTION

1. Oh, Bil - ly has a new shirt, a new shirt, a new shirt,

2. Oh, Ellen has a new dress, etc.
3. Oh, Charles has some new shoes, etc.

An interesting variation is:

Oh, Billy has a new walk (or jump, skip, hop),
A new walk, a new walk,
Oh, Billy has a new walk,
He'll show us all today.

Oh, Bil - ly has a new shirt, He wore to school to - day.

○ Counting Song

Words and Music by David Russell

WITH HUMOR

One, two, a cow says, "Moo!" Three, four, the li - ons roar!

Five, six, a mon-key does tricks! Sev-en, eight, who's sit-ting on the gate?

Nine, ten, a big fat hen! Start to count all o - ver a - gain!

The children may like to play rhythm instruments to this pattern:

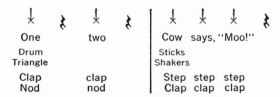

One	two	Cow says, "Moo!"
Drum		Sticks
Triangle		Shakers
Clap	clap	Step step step
Nod	nod	Clap clap clap

Playing the instruments may suggest rhythmic movements for some of the children while the others play.

7

A Fish Story

DRAMATICALLY

Mother Goose   Music by Anthony Burke

LOUD-SOFT   LOW-HIGH

One, two, three, four, five! I caught a fish a - live.

Six, sev-en, eight, nine, ten! I let it go a - gain.

Why did I let it go? Be-cause it hurt my fin-ger so!

Which fin-ger did it bite? The lit-tle one on the right.

Clap softly to loudly as the
    melody ascends (first phrase).
Clap loudly to softly as the
    melody descends (second phrase).
Rhythm instruments may also
    be used in the same way.
Clap low to high, and high
    to low with the melody.
You might like to try some
    movement with arms and feet also.

8

Five Little Alligators

Traditional Southern Singing Game

LOUD-SOFT   SLOW-FAST

LIVELY

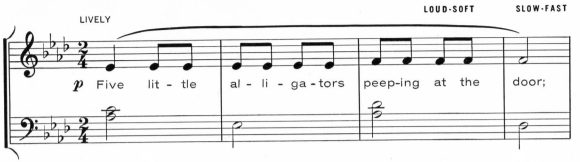

p Five lit-tle al-li-ga-tors peep-ing at the door;

One crawled a-way, and then there were four;

mf Al-li-ga-tor, al-li-ga-tor, hap-py and gay,

Al-li-ga-tor, al-li-ga-tor, crawl a-way.

This happy melody about happy alligators can be fun to sing because it is also a "counting out" song. Can the children think of any other animals to sing about? Kangaroos, monkeys, elephants? Anything else, such as steamboats or witches or reindeer? "Five little witches" at Halloween time would suggest a slower tempo and a softer tone to indicate "mystery."

9

Mother's Knives and Forks

Traditional Finger Game   Old American Song

WITH A SWING

These are moth-er's knives and forks, This is moth-er's ta - ble,

This is sis - ter's look - ing glass, This is the ba - by's cra - dle.

This and the next four songs are finger-play songs that have been loved by children for many years.

10

Knock at the Door

Traditional Finger Game   Traditional Song

PLAYFULLY

Knock at the door!
Tap forehead.

Peep in!
Point to eye.

Pull the latch and walk in!
Gently pull nose.   Put finger in mouth.

The Family

Traditional Finger Game   Old American Song

HAPPILY

This is our moth-er, This is our fa-ther, This is our broth-er tall,

This is our sis-ter, This is our ba-by, Oh, how we love them all!

11

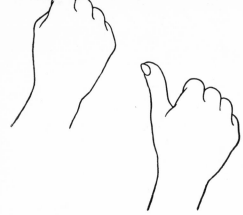

Where Is Thumbkin?

Traditional Finger Game   Traditional Song

FLOWINGLY

1. Where is thumb-kin? Where is thumb-kin? Here I am, here I am!

2. Where is pointer?
3. Where is tall man?
4. Where is ring man?
5. Where is little man?
6. Where's the family? (Here we are.)

You may like to vary this song by using the names of the children: Where is Mary? And so on.

How are you to-day, sir? Ver-y well, I thank you! Run a-way, run a-way!

Here Is the Church

Traditional Finger Game   Music by Richard C. Berg

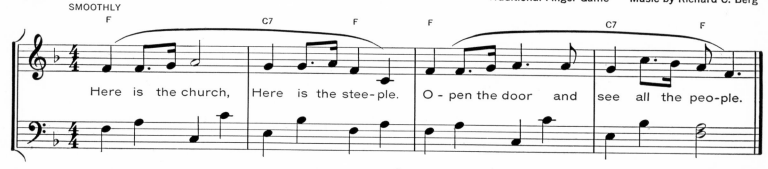

SMOOTHLY

Here is the church, Here is the stee-ple. O - pen the door and see all the peo-ple.

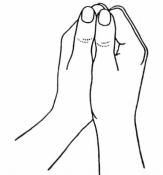

Time to Rise

Words by R. L. Stevenson   Music by Richard C. Berg

EASILY

A bird-ie with a yel-low bill Hopped up on my win-dow sill,

Cocked his shin-ing eye and said, "Ain't you 'shamed, you sleep-y head?"

Wake Me

Adapted from a Negro Folk Song

LIVELY

f 1. Wake me! Shake me! Don't let me sleep too late; —

Got to get up bright and ear-ly in the morn-ing, Going to swing on the gold-en gate.

2. Wake me! Shake me!
   Don't let me sleep too late;
   Got to comb my hair this morning,
   Going to swing on the golden gate.

3. Got to brush my teeth this morning.

4. Got to dress myself this morning.
   Can the children think of other activities?

Be Happy!

Words by R. L. Stevenson   Music by Richard C. Berg

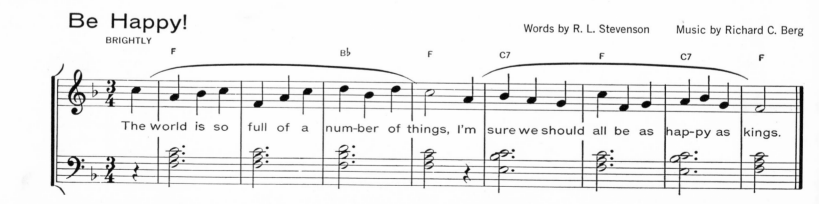

BRIGHTLY

The world is so full of a num-ber of things, I'm sure we should all be as hap-py as kings.

What Time Is It?

Words and Music by Daniel Hooley

All: The clock on the shelf is strik - ing! What time can it be?

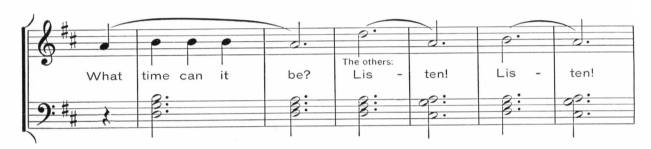

What time can it be? *The others:* Lis - ten! Lis - ten!

Bells, triangle, piano

One child plays the instrument. It's five o' clock! (four, six, etc.)

The child who takes the solo part may make it any time he chooses. The class silently count the number of times he plays the chord, or sounds the bells or triangle, in order to announce the correct time in the last phrase of the song.

If the child uses the piano to sound the time, he may use any two notes high on the keyboard that sound well together, not necessarily D and F#.

15

Telephone

Words and Music by Daniel Hooley

LOUD-SOFT

LIGHTLY

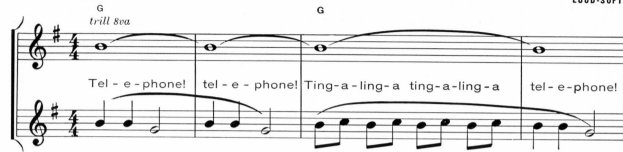

Tel - e - phone! tel - e - phone! Ting-a-ling-a ting-a-ling-a tel - e - phone!

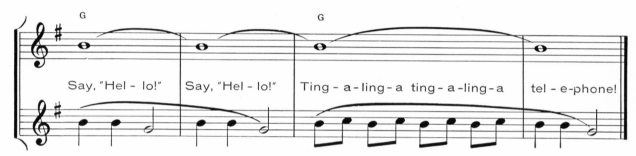

Say, "Hel - lo!" Say, "Hel - lo!" Ting - a - ling - a ting - a - ling - a tel - e - phone!

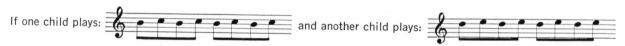

If one child plays: and another child plays:

together, they can make a fine tinga-linga which can ring all through the song. Or one pattern alone may be used. The two patterns need not be synchronized.

Sing about a telephone near at hand and a telephone far away in the house that can be only faintly heard.

Dial the Number

Words and Music by Robert Pace

IMAGINATIVELY

Di-al the num-ber, zip-buzz-a - ree! "May I speak to Bil - ly?" "This is he."

The Washing Machine

Words by Ilo Orleans   Music by Philip Gordon

STEADILY

mf The wash-ing ma-chine, the wash-ing ma-chine, My clothes go in dirt-y, my clothes come out clean;

Such won-der-ful mag-ic I nev-er have seen, The wash-ing ma-chine, the wash-ing ma-chine.

Seated, the children may imitate the rotation of the washer with their
arms. Standing, they may turn in one direction for the first two phrases
and turn in the other for the last two phrases.

Be Polite!

Old Saying   Music by Daniel Hooley

SIMPLY

Po - lite-ness is to do and say The kind-est things in the kind - est way.

Lady, Lady!

Words and Music by Melissa Murphy

NOT FAST

Lady, Lady, Buy a broom for your ba - by;

Sweep him low and sweep him high, And sweep the cob-webs out of the sky;

Lady, Lady, Buy a broom for your ba - by!

Sing the song slowly as a lullaby. Then sing it a little faster as a dance tune. Bells or the piano can play these two notes on "Lady, Lady":

A C

The triangle may also sound on "Lady, Lady."

Mocking-Bird Lullaby

American Play-Party Song

QUIETLY
F ... C7 ... C7 ... F

mp 1. Hush, lit-tle ba - by, don't say a word, Dad-dy's going to buy you a mock-ing bird,

C7 ... F

If that mock-ing bird can't sing, Daddy's going to buy you a dia-mond ring.

2. If that diamond ring turns brass,
   Daddy's going to buy you a looking-glass;
   If that looking-glass gets broke,
   Daddy's going to buy you a billy goat.

3. If that billy goat won't pull,
   Daddy's going to buy you a cart and bull;
   If that cart and bull turns over,
   Daddy's going to buy you a dog named Rover.

4. If that dog named Rover won't bark,
   Daddy's going to buy you a pony cart;
   If that pony cart falls down,
   You'll be the nicest boy (**or** girl) in town.

My Kitten

Words by Julie Gibault   Music by Josephine Wolverton

EASILY

1. My lit-tle kit-ten likes to play When I come home from school each day.

2. My little kitten likes to purr
   While I sit by and smooth her fur.

3. My little kitten, soft as silk,
   Miaows to get her bowl of milk.

19

My Tree House

Words by Josephine Wolverton   Czech Folk Tune

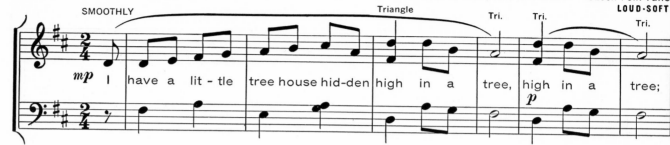

I have a lit-tle tree house hid-den high in a tree, high in a tree;

Birds are sing-ing all a-round me, They sing to me, they sing to me.

Try for an echo effect on the repetition of the words "high in a tree" and "they sing to me."

Mammy Loves

Southern Folk Song

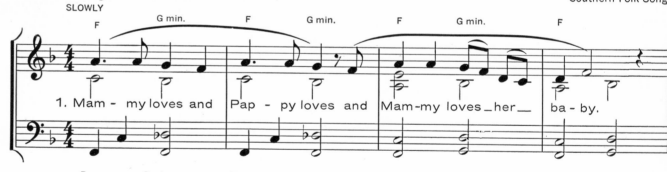

1. Mam - my loves and Pap - py loves and Mam-my loves her baby.

Go to sleep-y, go to sleep, Go to sleep, you lit-tle ba-by.

2. Lullaby and lullaby
   And lullaby, my little baby,
   Lullaby and lullaby,
   Lullaby, my little baby.

3. (Hum the melody softly.)

4. (Repeat the first stanza.)

20

Helping Mother

Words and Music by Daniel Hooley

LIGHTLY

1. Help your moth-er set the ta-ble With a knife and fork and spoon;
2. Help your moth-er clear the ta-ble, Take the knife and fork and spoon;

Help your moth-er set the ta-ble Ev-'ry aft-er-noon.
Help your moth-er clear the ta-ble Morn-ing, night, and noon.

My Prayer

Traditional Words   Music by DuWard Whelchel

QUIETLY

p Now I lay me down to sleep, I pray Thee, Lord, my soul to keep;

Thy love stay with me thro' the night And wake me with the morn-ing light.

21

The Postman

Words by Ellen Hertzler   Music by Florence White

The postman whistles, the postman sings, From house to house the mail he brings;

*Use the term "mailman" if it is preferred to "postman" in your community.

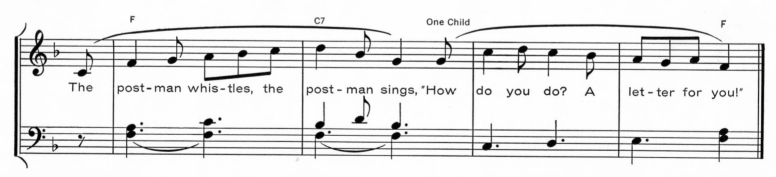

The postman whistles, the postman sings, "How do you do? A letter for you!"

The postman walks in different ways. How does he walk with a heavy load? With a light load? How does he walk when he is in a hurry? When he is very tired?

Try starting the song quite softly, as though the postman were far down the street. Let the song get louder as the postman nears your house.

The Laundry Man

Words by Marianne St. John   Music by David Russell

1-2. What shall we give to the laun-dry man? What shall we give to the laun-dry man?

1. Fa-ther's shirts and Moth-er's — skirts, That's what we'll give to the laun-dry man.
2. Ba-by's bib and sheets from the crib, That's what we'll give to the laun-dry man.

The Traffic Policeman

Words by Julie Gibault   Music by R. A. Coan

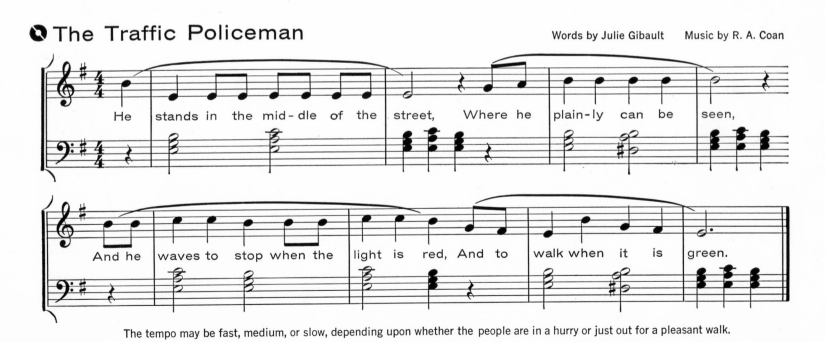

He stands in the mid-dle of the street, Where he plain-ly can be seen,

And he waves to stop when the light is red, And to walk when it is green.

The tempo may be fast, medium, or slow, depending upon whether the people are in a hurry or just out for a pleasant walk.

Fire-Truck Song

Words and Music by Daniel Hooley

BRISKLY

All: Ding ding ding ding ding! Here comes the fire truck, the fire truck!

Ding ding ding ding ding! Get out of the way!

Where is the fire? Where is the fire?

Several children chug around the room as the fire truck. Behind them is the "fireman" looking for the fire. The child selected to sing the solo part stands by his desk and points to his "house" as he sings. Fireman and fire truck go to the house, put out the fire, and then chug back to their own places.

Other children may ring bells or strike triangles as alarms. Some of them may pretend they are driving the fire truck.

These notes may be played throughout the song:

Make the "ding-ding" sound high up on the piano keys with this note, or use the triangle for it:

Steam Shovel

Words by Daniel Hooley   Theme collected by Béla Bartók

DELIBERATELY

D minor

This is how the steam shov-el works!

This is how the steam shov-el works!

Picks up dirt and then it dumps it! Picks up dirt and then it dumps it!

I Need a Haircut

Words by Julie Gibault   Scandinavian Folk Tune

WITH HUMOR

F

I need a brand-new hair-cut, My moth-er told me so; I'll climb up in the bar ber chair

26

Be - fore more hair has time to grow. A snip! Snip! A snip-snip-snip!

When the song is repeated, you might sing "A buzz, buzz," etc. on the last two measures.

The Delivery Boy

Words and Music by Daniel Hooley
LOUD-SOFT

1. Knock, knock, knock, Knock, knock, knock, Who's knock-ing at the door?
2. Knock, knock, knock, Knock, knock, knock, What will he bring to eat?

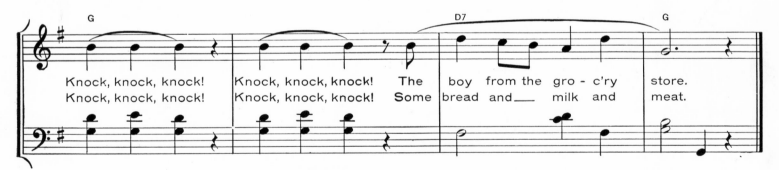

Knock, knock, knock! Knock, knock, knock! The boy from the gro - c'ry store.
Knock, knock, knock! Knock, knock, knock! Some bread and___ milk and meat.

Try loud knocks and soft knocks.

Use the following for an Introduction
and let it play throughout the song:

Wood Block

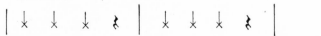

If the delivery boy rings the bell instead
of knocking, use this Introduction:

Bell

"Who's ring - ing at the door?"

When I Am Big

Words and Music by Josephine Wolverton

GAILY

When I am big, I'll own a car And ride a-bout the town;

I'll buy some gas to make it go, And ride up hill and down.

28

Streamline Train

Words and Music by First-grade Children

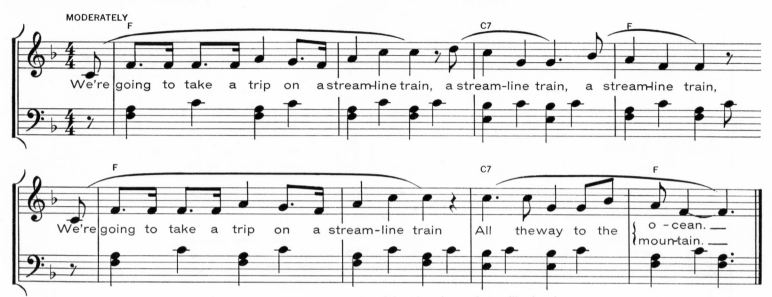

We're going to take a trip on a stream-line train, a stream-line train, a stream-line train,

We're going to take a trip on a stream-line train All the way to the { o-cean. / moun-tain.

Other stanzas may be added describing the trip or what we'll take along.

When the Train Comes Along

Adapted from a Negro Folk Song

1. When the train comes a-long,—When the train comes a-long,

I'll meet you at the sta-tion When the train comes a-long. Whoo-hoo!

2. When the plane comes along, etc.
3. When the bus comes along, etc.
4. When the truck comes along, etc.
5. When the 'copter comes along, etc.
6. When Jack comes along, etc.,
   I'll meet him at the station.
7. When Sally comes along, etc.,
   I'll meet her at the station.

Choo Choo!

Words by Julie Gibault   French Nursery Tune

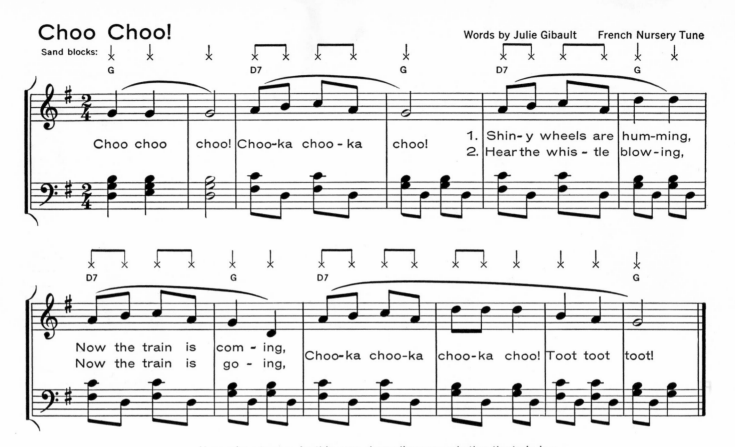

Choo choo choo! Choo-ka choo-ka choo!

1. Shin-y wheels are hum-ming,
2. Hear the whis-tle blow-ing,

Now the train is com-ing,
Now the train is go-ing,

Choo-ka choo-ka choo-ka choo! Toot toot toot!

Use various tempos for this song, depending upon whether the train is a
fast one or a slow one; whether the train is gathering speed or slowing down.

I Like a Bike

Words and Music by David Russell

HAPPILY

I like a bike! I ped-al fast or slow;

I like a bike! I ride where I want to go.

The Big Truck

Words and Music by Robert Pace

LOUD-SOFT

HEAVILY

Down the high-way, here it comes! Bright and shin-ing, big and strong!

Let the children find places in the song to go from soft to loud.

The truck moves heavily if it has a heavy load. It moves lightly if it has a light load.

Put on brakes

Up the hill and 'round a curve, The big truck, the big truck, the big truck! Now stop!

31

Sailing

Words by Anne Beyer   Music by David Russell

SWAYING

SMOOTHLY, RATHER SLOWLY

Sail - ing out to sea, ___ Sail - ing out so far, ___

I can al - most touch my sail Up a - gainst a star! ___

The children may make sails by raising their arms over their heads, with palms to-gether. They sway gently in the breeze.

Little Ships

Words by Joan Hurst   German Folk Tune

FLOWINGLY

Here and there, here and there, Lit - tle ships sail on the sea;

Here and there, here and there, Lit - tle ships sail on the sea.

Pull the Oars

Words and Music by Richard C. Berg

SLOWLY, WELL ACCENTED

Use a strong, forceful movement to pull the oars.

Pull the oars with stead-y beat, Oh, pull the oars with me!

Soon we'll reach the dis-tant shore, So pull the oars with me!

Tugboats

Words and Music by Robert Pace

SLOW-FASTER

WELL ACCENTED

Tug-boats whis-tle and tug-boats groan, Churn the wa-ter and make white foam;

Tug-boats push — and tug-boats pull Big ships and barg-es load-ed full.

Pull a boat carrying iron. Pull a boat carrying feathers.

Movement:			
Pull	(rest)	Pull	(rest)
Chant:			
Chug	chug	Chug	chug
Sand blocks:			
Tug-boats whis-tle and		tug-boats groan	

33

The Horn on the Bus

Words by Susan Rupert   Music by Cecilia Johns

Hear the horn on the bus! It's a warn-ing to us to get out of the way!

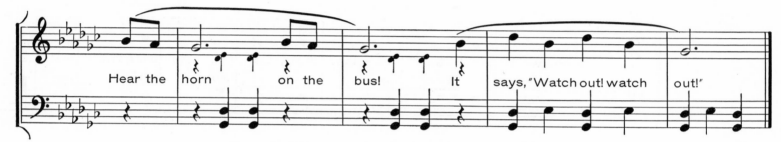

Hear the horn on the bus! It says, "Watch out! watch out!"

Five or six children may make a bus (single file, hands on the shoulders of the child in front). The child at the head of the file may be the driver.

ON THE BLACK KEYS

The piano can make the noise of the wheels down low on the keyboard.
It can make the noise of the horn in the middle of the keyboard.
It can make the swish-swish of the windshield wiper on the bus high on the keyboard.

After the children have learned the song, two or three may help make the honk-honk of the bus (small notes).

 ## Palomino

Words and Music by Robert Pace

I'm rid-ing a bright pal-o-mi-no, Pal-o-mi-no, pal-o-mi-no!

34

I'm rid-ing a bright pal-o-mi-no, I'm rid-ing all o-ver the range.

quickly **2.** I'm riding a big, bucking bronco, etc.,
I'm riding all over the range.

moderately **3.** I'm sitting up high in the saddle, etc.,
I'm riding all over the **range.**

Let the children use wood blocks, coconut shells, or any cardboard containers, turned upside down and struck on the floor in this rhythm throughout:

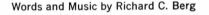

They may show how they would ride a tired pony, a pony hurrying home for his oats, and a pony rounding up the cattle.

🎵 Galloping

Words and Music by Richard C. Berg

Gal-lop-ing, gal-lop-ing down the road, Down the road, down the road!

Gal-lop-ing, gal-lop-ing on my horse, A-go-ing down the road.

The children will find many ways to gallop, perhaps like a little Shetland pony, a circus pony, a work horse, or a race horse.

You may want to use this song for experience in various rhythms. If so, add as a second stanza: "walking, walking," etc. As a third, try "trotting, trotting," etc. Return to "galloping" for a fourth.

The record will help you with the tempos.

Wait for the Wagon

Adapted Words   Music by R. B. Buckley

1. Wait for the wag-on, Wait for the wag-on,

Wait for the wag-on and we'll all take a ride;

Climb in the wag-on, Climb in the wag-on,

2. Wait for the airplane, etc., and we'll all take a ride;
   Get in the airplane, etc., and we'll all take a ride.

3. Wait for the steamboat, etc., and we'll all take a ride;
   Sail on the steamboat and we'll all take a ride.

4. Wait for the fire truck, etc., and we'll all take a ride;
   Sit in the fire truck and we'll all take a ride.

   Some child may pretend to be the wagon, air-plane, steamboat, or the fire truck and lead the rest.

Climb in the wag-on and we'll all take a ride.

36

Bumbershoot

Words and Music by Robert Pace

Push up your bum-ber-shoot! (A plip - plop! A pit - ter-pat!)

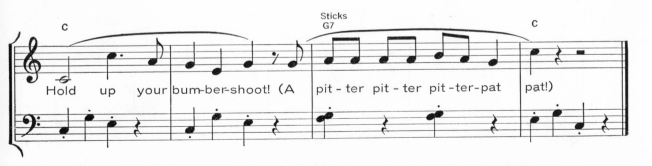

Hold up your bum-ber-shoot! (A pit - ter pit - ter pit -ter-pat pat!)

2. "Squish! Squash!" galoshes say,
(A plip-plop! A pitter-pat!)
"Squish! Squash!" galoshes say,
"A rainy, rainy, rainy day!"

Bumbershoot, a humorous term for "umbrella," is a popular word in many parts of our country.

Push up the umbrella on the first and third phrases. The raindrops may be loud or soft. For the sound of galoshes, use sand blocks.

37

Rain

Traditional Rhyme   Music by Josephine Wolverton

Rain on the green grass, Rain on the tree, Rain on the house-top, But not on me!

Sticks may be used to make a light "drip-drop" throughout. Change the tempo and make a downpour.

Use C and G bells or triangles.

Listen to the Rain!

Words and Music by David Russell

Lis-ten!   Lis-ten!   Lis-ten to the rain!

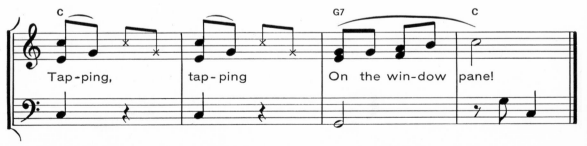

Tap-ping,   tap-ping   On the win-dow pane!

38

Thunder

Words and Music by David Russell

MYSTERIOUSLY

Drum   Drum

Boo-oo-oom! Boo-oo-oom! Hear the thun-der roar! I used to run when I heard it,

But I nev-er do an-y more.

Drum   Drum

Boo-oo-oom! Boo-oo-oom!

Make the thunder by patting both palms on the drum. Make the thunder nearby and far away. Tapping gently with flat fingers on a hard-covered book gives a sound of thunder, too.

Bright Star

Words and Music by Lydia Foote

SLOWLY

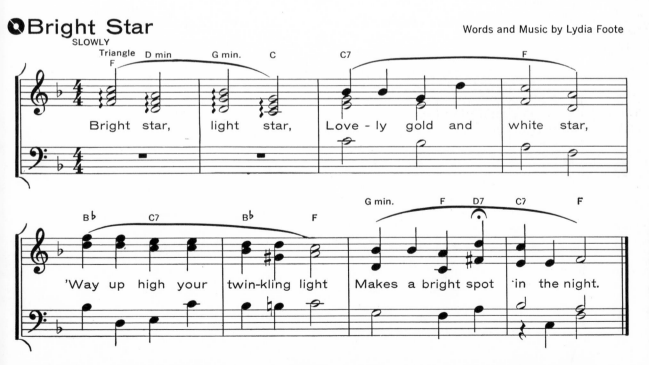

Triangle
F   D min   G min.   C   C7   F

Bright star,   light star,   Love-ly gold and   white star,

B♭   C7   B♭   F   G min.   F   D7   C7   F

'Way up high your   twin-kling light   Makes a bright spot   in the night.

39

A Tree Grows Straight Words and Music by May Todd

SLOWLY

A tree grows straight and tall,

It lifts its branch-es high!

A tree bends with the wind, _____

And tries to touch the sky, _____ And tries to touch the sky.

Encourage the children to let the words suggest movement.

Leaves

Words and Music by Josephine Wolverton

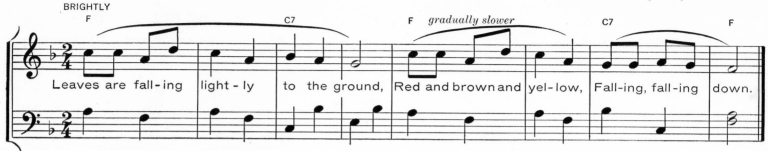

Leaves are fall-ing light-ly to the ground, Red and brown and yel-low, Fall-ing, fall-ing down.

Let the children gently imitate the falling leaves.

The North Wind

Words by Lou Ann Hatcher   Music by Roger Elston

Whoeee, whoeee, whoeee, brrr! North wind blow-ing, hear it call-ing "whoeee, brrr!"

Children enjoy coming in on the third measure with shakers.
See that they do not shake too hard to spoil the mood.

The North Wind's Song

Words and Music by Josephine Wolverton

Ooo — Ooo — The North Wind sings a lone-some tune. Ooo — Ooo-Cold win-ter's com-ing soon.

Old Mother Goose

Folk Rhyme   Old Tune

WITH A SWING

1. Old Moth-er Goose is pick-ing her geese,
2. Old Moth-er Goose is mak-ing it snow,

Pick-ing her geese, pick-ing her geese,
Mak-ing it snow, mak-ing it snow;

Old Moth-er Goose is pick-ing her geese,
Old Moth-er Goose is mak-ing it snow,

And throw-ing the feath-ers a - way.
She's mak-ing it snow to - day.

A Scandinavian legend explains snowflakes: they are the feathers that an
old woman in the sky picks from her geese and throws away.

43

○ The Shivers

Words and Music by Daniel Hooley

LOUD-SOFT

The wind is cold! Shiv-er, shiv-er, Brrr! The wind is cold! Shiv-er, shiv-er, Brrr!

I will keep my coat all but-toned, So that I'll be nice and warm,

But the wind is cold! Shiv-er, shiv-er, Brrr! The wind is cold! Shiv-er, shiv-er, Brrr!

Play the sticks loudly, and the shakers softly.

44

Spring

Words and Music by Daniel Hooley

SIMPLY
Bells or Piano

"Cheep, cheep!" Why do the birds sing? "Cheep, cheep!" Why do the birds sing?

"Cheep, cheep!" The birds all sing "Cheep, cheep, cheep!" be - cause it's spring.

Spring Is Coming

Anonymous   Music by Josephine Wolverton

SIMPLY

Spring is com-ing! Spring is com-ing! How do you think I know?

The daf - fo - dils are bloom-ing, And I know it must be so.

45

The Robin's Song

Adapted Words   German Folk Tune

WITH A BOUNCE

1. The rob-in now is call - ing, I hear his hap-py song; ___
2. "Cheer up! Cheer up!" he's call - ing, I hear his hap-py song; ___

Come, sing with Rob - in Red - breast, For spring has come a - long. ___
"Cheer up! Cheer up!" he's call - ing, For spring has come a - long. ___

Let the children hear the recording before you teach the song.

Let's Plant a Tree

Words by Marianne St. John   Music by David Russell

LIGHTLY

Let's plant a seed-ling tree, A lit - tle seed-ling tree;

Some day when it grows up there'll be shade for you and me.

Roll That Red Ball

Illinois Game Song

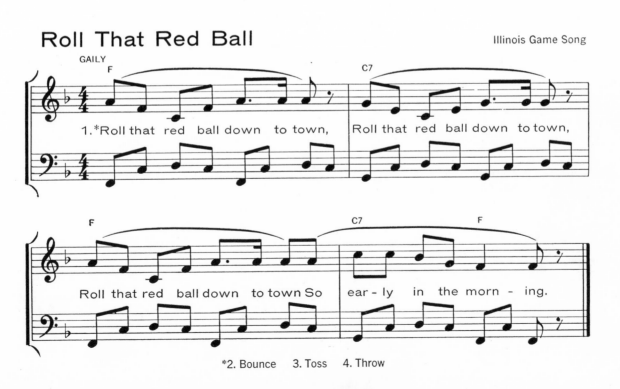

GAILY

1.*Roll that red ball down to town, Roll that red ball down to town,

Roll that red ball down to town So ear-ly in the morn-ing.

*2. Bounce   3. Toss   4. Throw

Step and Clap

Words by Anne Beyer   Music by Elsie Smith

LIGHTLY

1. Step, step, clap, clap! Step, step, clap, clap! Turn your-self a-round and then you clap, clap, clap!

2. Bend and clap, clap,
   Bend and clap, clap, etc.

3. Hands up! Clap, clap,
   Hands up! Clap, clap, etc.

4. Stoop down, clap, clap,
   Stoop down, clap, clap,
   Turn yourself around,
   And then you clap, clap, clap.

5. Repeat Stanza 1 to end the song.

To vary the song, try either or both of the following:

1. Let everyone sing the first and last stanzas, but have the second, third, and fourth stanzas sung and acted by three different groups from the class.

2. Let the boys sing "Step, step" and the girls sing "clap, clap" in the first and last stanzas. In the other stanzas, the boys sing only (2) "Bend and," (3) "Hands up," and (4) "Stoop down."

Robot

Words and Music by Daniel Hooley

MECHANICALLY
Sticks throughout

Ro-bot, ro-bot, me-chan-i-cal man, Clank, clank, clank! He's a walk-ing tin can;

Staccato throughout

Noth-ing could be more clum-sy than Ro-bot, ro-bot, me-chan-i-cal man.

Let Us Dance Together

Guatemalan School Song

HAPPILY

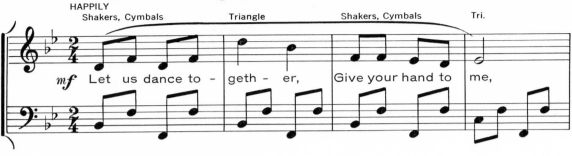

Shakers, Cymbals   Triangle   Shakers, Cymbals   Tri.

mf Let us dance to - geth - er, Give your hand to me,

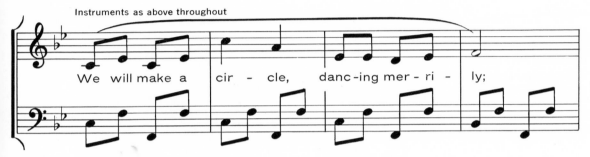

Instruments as above throughout

We will make a cir - cle, danc-ing mer - ri - ly;

Lis - ten to the mu - sic, What a hap - py sound!

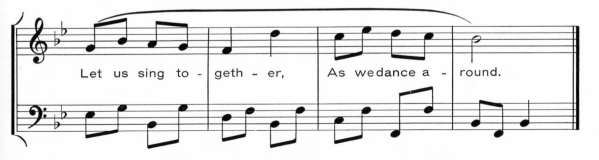

Let us sing to - geth - er, As we dance a - round.

Try other combinations of rhythm instruments. For instance, one combination may play the first half of the song, while a second combination plays the last half.

Whether you have everybody in a big circle or whether you form smaller circles of two's and four's, let the children make up their own steps.

49

My Fiddle

WITH AN EASY SWING

Adapted Version of an Old Song

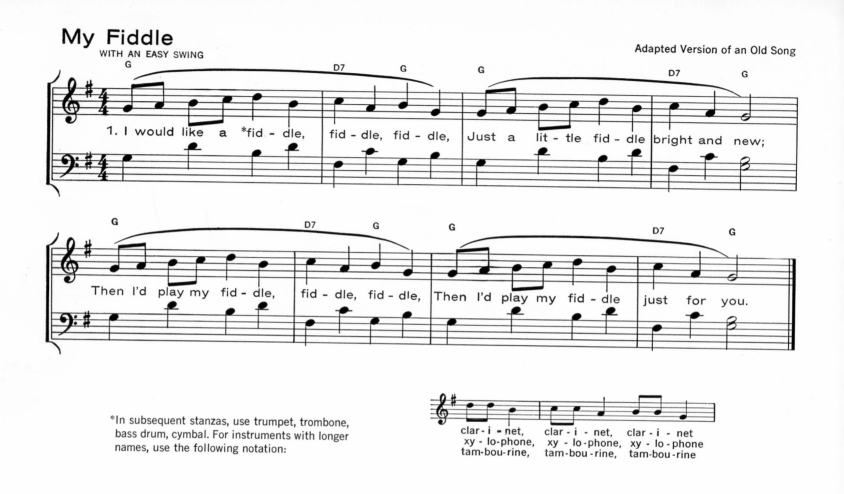

1. I would like a *fid - dle, fid - dle, fid - dle, Just a lit - tle fid - dle bright and new;

Then I'd play my fid - dle, fid - dle, fid - dle, Then I'd play my fid - dle just for you.

*In subsequent stanzas, use trumpet, trombone, bass drum, cymbal. For instruments with longer names, use the following notation:

clar - i - net, clar - i - net, clar - i - net
xy - lo - phone, xy - lo - phone, xy - lo - phone
tam - bou - rine, tam - bou - rine, tam - bou - rine

What Shall We Do?

Words by Anita Alexander   Music by Robert Pace

EASILY

mf

1. What shall we do, and where shall we go? Will it be fast, or will it be slow?
2. See what we do, and see where we go? Some-times it's fast, and some-times it's slow.

50

It will be fun, what-ev-er we do, So show us a mo-tion, we'll fol-low you.
Is-n't it fun, what-ev-er we do? So here is a mo-tion that we can do.

After Stanza 1, you might say "Let's swing." Everybody swings to the music and then goes on to Stanza 2. Or you might say, "Let's skip." Or "Let's jump," or "Let's turn around."

Simon Says

Words and Music by Roger Elston

STEADILY

Si-mon says to do the way that he will do:

For an uninterrupted activity, choose five or six children to take turns being "Simon" before beginning to sing. Then sing the song five or six times with no pause between repetitions. "Simon" must keep his activities in time with the music. Choose a child with a good sense of rhythm to lead off.

Do this, do that, do this, do that! Oh, Si-mon tells us what to do.

When We March

WITH A SWING

Adapted Words   American Folk Tune

f 1. Oh, when we march___ a-round the world,___ Oh, when we march a-round the world,___

Oh, don't you want to march 'round with us, When we march a-round the world?

Use rhythm instruments and march in a parade.

2. Oh, when we clap (⅄ ⅄) our hands like this (⅄ ⅄).

3. Oh, when we jump (⅄ ⅄) our feet like this (⅄ ⅄).

4. Oh, when we wave our hands up high.

5. Oh, when we skip around the moon.

Blind Man's Buff

Words by Robert Pace   Music adapted from Béla Bartók

Cov - er your eyes! Please do not peek! Turn a-round and 'round and 'round and then go seek!

Who will it be? Who will it be? You are get-ting clos-er, clos-er, Don't touch me! Don't touch me!

Stand Up and Look

Words and Music by Roger Elston

Stand up and look a-round, Shake your head and turn a-round;

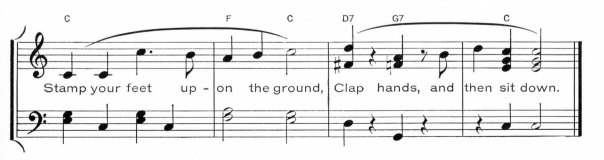

Stamp your feet up-on the ground, Clap hands, and then sit down.

Use this song as a directed activity. It is useful when children have become tired or restless.

53

Jim-along, Josie

Traditional American Folk Game

1. Hey, Jim a-long, Jim a-long, Jo-sie, Hey, Jim a-long, Jim a-long, Joe!

Hey, Jim a-long, Jim a-long, Jo-sie, Hey, Jim a-long, Jim a-long, Joe!

Face to the cen-ter, Hands on your knees! Clap three times and turn a-round, please!

slowly 2. Strut, Jim-a-long, Jim-a-long, Josie, etc.

fast 3. Tiptoe along, Jim-a-long, Josie, etc.

fast 4. Run, Jim-a-long, Jim-a-long, Josie, etc.

fast 5. Jump, Jim-a-long, Jim-a-long, Josie, etc.

6. Do what you want, Jim-a-long, Josie, etc.

If the game is "danced" in a circle, let the circle move in a different direction for each stanza.

The Merry-Go-Round

Words and Music by Richard C. Berg

The hors-es on the mer-ry-go-round Go up and down and a-round and 'round;

As I ride a-round on the mer-ry-go-round, My horse goes up and down.

Have the children form a circle like a merry-go-round, facing counterclockwise. They use an up-and-down movement, imitating the horses on the merry-go-round as they move around the circle.

Wind the Bobbin

Georgia Singing Game

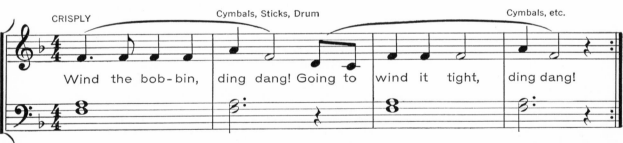

Wind the bob-bin, ding dang! Going to wind it tight, ding dang!

A line of boys and girls wind around a leader, making a spiral for-mation.

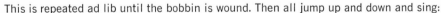

This is repeated ad lib until the bobbin is wound. Then all jump up and down and sing:

A bobbin is a spool or reel on which thread or yarn is wound.

Bob-bin a wound up, Bob-bin a wound up, Bob-bin a wound up, Break it!

The group scatters.

55

The Wiggle Song

2. My thumbs and fingers are wiggling, etc.

3. My hand is starting to wiggle, etc.

4. My arms are starting to wiggle, etc.

5. My head is starting to wiggle, etc.

6. Now all of me is a-wiggling, etc.

FREELY

1. My thumbs are start-ing to wig-gle, My thumbs are start-ing to wig-gle,

My thumbs are start-ing to wig-gle A-round, a-round, a-round.—

On the Prairie

Words by Daniel Hooley   English Folk Tune

SLOWLY AND EASILY

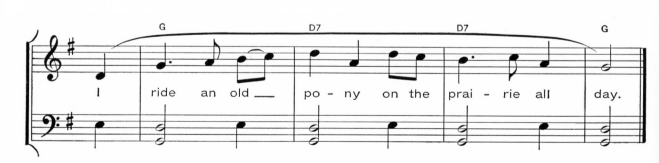

1. I ride an old __ po-ny on the prai-rie, on the prai-rie,

I ride an old __ po-ny on the prai-rie all day.

fast 2. I chase the stray dogies on the prairie, etc.

fast 3. I rope them with my lasso on the prairie, etc.

slow 4. At night I make a campfire on the prairie, etc.

As an accompaniment, use coconut shells or upturned cardboard cartons struck on the floor.

Green Grass

WITH A LILT

Early American Folk Song

LOUD-SOFT

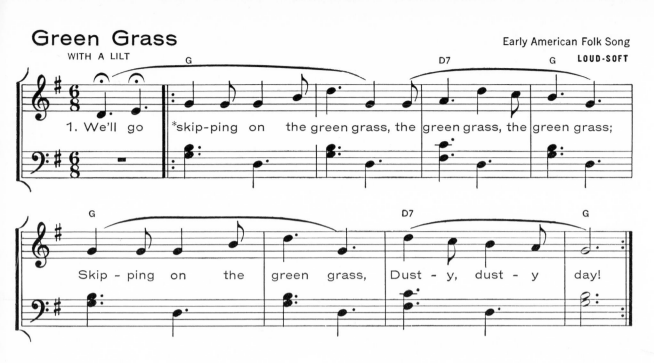

1. We'll go *skip-ping on the green grass, the green grass, the green grass;

Skip - ping on the green grass, Dust - y, dust - y day!

See the Puppets

WELL ACCENTED

Words by David Russell   French Folk Tune

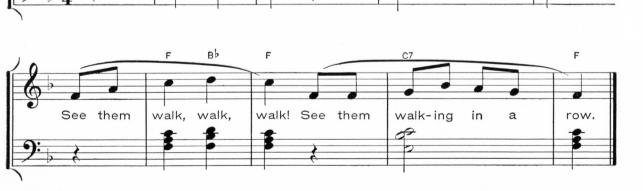

1. See them *walk, walk, walk! See the lit - tle walk-ing pup-pets,

See them walk, walk, walk! See them walk-ing in a row.

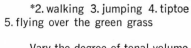

*2. walking 3. jumping 4. tiptoe
5. flying over the green grass

Vary the degree of tonal volume with each stanza.

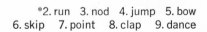

*2. run 3. nod 4. jump 5. bow
6. skip 7. point 8. clap 9. dance

This song is a favorite with children because of the variety of movement it allows. Encourage them to change the speed of movement with the different stanzas.

57

Long Summer Day

Traditional Rhyme   American Folk Song

EASILY

1. Walk and talk to-geth-er on a long sum-mer day, Walk and talk to-geth-er on a long sum-mer day.

2. Skip around together, etc.   3. Run around, etc.   4. Hop around, etc.   5. Turn around, etc.

Fingers, Nose, and Toes

Traditional Words and Tune

LIGHTLY

1. Put your fin-gers on your nose, then your toes, ___ Put your fin-gers on your nose, then your toes, ___

Put your fin-gers on your nose, Put your fin-gers on your nose,

Put your fin-gers on your nose and then your toes. ___

2. Put your fingers on your nose, then
   your cheeks,
   Put your fingers on your nose, then
   your cheeks,
   Put your fingers on your cheeks and
   then leave them there for weeks,
   Put your fingers on your nose and then
   your cheeks.

3. Put your fingers on your nose, then
   your hair,
   Put your fingers on your nose, then
   your hair,
   Put your fingers on your hair and then
   wave them in the air,
   Put your fingers on your nose and then
   your hair.

Hoppy, the Kangaroo

Words and Music by Daniel Hooley

LIGHTLY

1. Hop-sky hop! Hop-sky boo! Here comes Hop-py, the Kan - ga-roo.
2. Hop-sky hop! Hop-sky boo! I like Hop-py, the Kan - ga-roo.

Hop-sky hop! Hop-sky boo! Hop-ping his hop-pi - ty way to you.
Hop-sky hop! Hop-sky boo! Hop-pi - ty Hop-py, the Kan-ga-roo!

The children may jump high and jump low. They may
jump far and near, sideways, forward, backward, or in place.

Cows in the Pasture

Words and Music by Ernest Nelson

LAZILY

1. Cows are eat-ing the grass in the pas-ture, Cows are eat-ing the grass in the pas-ture,
2. Cow-bells ring, ding-a - ding, in the pas-ture, Cow-bells ring, ding-a - ding, in the pas-ture,

Cows are eat-ing the grass in the pas-ture, All of the live - long day.
Cow-bells ring, ding-a - ding, in the pas-ture, All of the live-long day.

Use a triangle or a cow bell on the second stanza.

Little Bunny Rabbit

Words and Music by Richard C. Berg

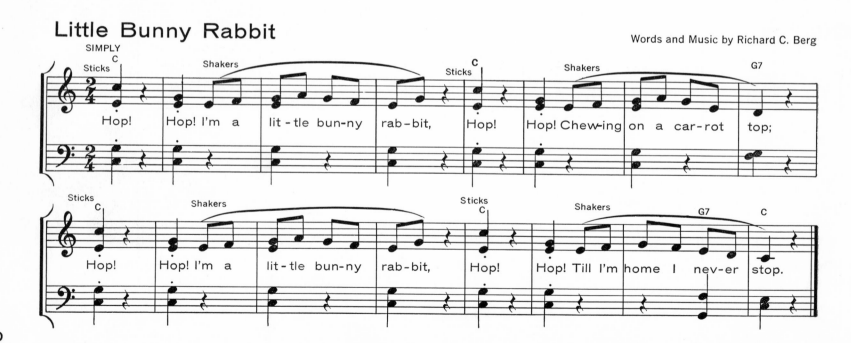

SIMPLY

Sticks · Shakers · Sticks · Shakers

Hop! Hop! I'm a lit-tle bun-ny rab-bit, Hop! Hop! Chew-ing on a car-rot top;

Sticks · Shakers · Sticks · Shakers

Hop! Hop! I'm a lit-tle bun-ny rab-bit, Hop! Hop! Till I'm home I nev-er stop.

60

Lipperty Lop

Words and Music by Ernest Nelson

Lip-per-ty lop, lip-per-ty lop, The rab-bit ran down to the car-rot shop;

He bought some car-rots and start-ed for home, Lip-per-ty, lip-per-ty lop!

A bear might go bumpety-bop to the honey shop. A bear walks slowly, while a rabbit hops fast.

How many stanzas can your children add to this song? The children may use sticks, a wood block, or a drum to play for the rabbits, bears, and other animals they may think of.

Panda

Words by Marianne St. John   Music by Daniel Hooley

SLOWLY

Gi-ant ba - by pan-da comes from a-cross the seas;

Gi-ant ba - by pan-da comes from Chi-na, if you please.

This melody can be played with just five black keys.

Impersonating the waddling walk of the panda should be fun.

61

The Elephant

Words and Music by Daniel Hooley

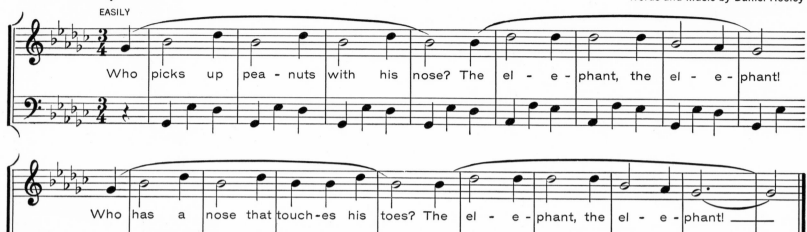

Who picks up pea-nuts with his nose? The el - e - phant, the el - e - phant!

Who has a nose that touch-es his toes? The el - e - phant, the el - e - phant!

Children enjoy playing "elephant," swinging their "trunks" on the accented beats as they lumber along.

Clumpity Clump

Words and Music by Richard C. Berg

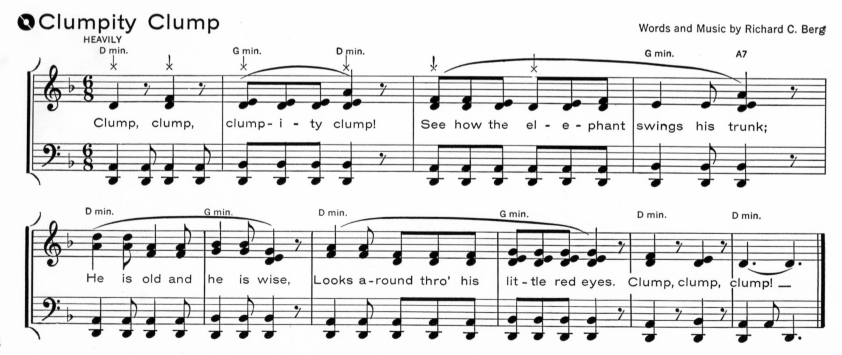

Clump, clump, clump-i-ty clump! See how the el - e - phant swings his trunk;

He is old and he is wise, Looks a-round thro' his lit - tle red eyes. Clump, clump, clump!

62

Just Like This

Words and Music by Elsie Smith

SLOWLY

1. The el - e-phant's trunk sways just like this when he walks,—

The el - e-phant's trunk sways just like this when he walks.—

2. The bun - ny hops, the bun - ny hops just like this. —

The bun - ny hops, the bun - ny hops just like this. —

3. The airplane flies,
   The airplane flies
   Just like this.

4. The cowboy rides,
   The cowboy rides
   Just like this.

5. I like to skip,
   I like to skip
   Just like this.

The children move in a circle for this song.

63

Never Did I See!

Words and Music by Stephen Scott

HUMOROUSLY

Nev-er did I see such a sight! Nev-er did I see such a sight!

Nev-er did I see such a sight! An el-e-phant rid-ing on a fire truck!

On the fourth phrase, sing:
2. A turtle sitting in a steamboat.
3. A monkey playing on a trumpet.

Can your children add other stanzas?

The Giraffe

Words and Music by Marie Grosjean

NOT FAST

A gi-raffe can't laugh, A gi-raffe can't sing, A gi-raffe can't do much of an-y-thing

Each child holds an arm up high to make a long neck for the giraffe.

But walk a - round like this, But walk a - round like this!

Teddy Bear

Rope-jumping Chant

SMOOTHLY

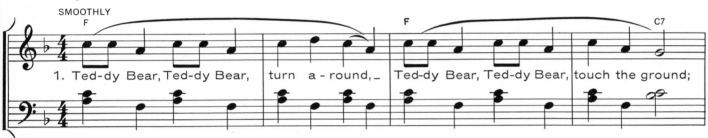

1. Ted-dy Bear, Ted-dy Bear, turn a - round, — Ted-dy Bear, Ted-dy Bear, touch the ground;

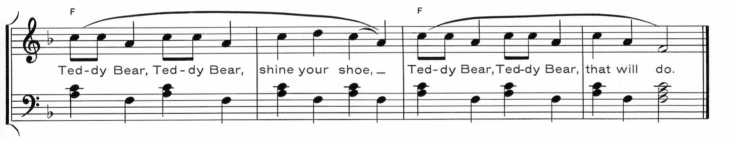

Ted-dy Bear, Ted-dy Bear, shine your shoe, — Ted-dy Bear, Ted-dy Bear, that will do.

2. Teddy Bear, Teddy Bear, walk upstairs,
   Teddy Bear, Teddy Bear, say your prayers,
   Teddy Bear, Teddy Bear, switch off your light,
   Teddy Bear, Teddy Bear, say good-night.

   Here are other ways to play this game:

1. Try soft little jumps on the first two phrases; make bigger
   jumps on the third and fourth phrases.

2. Try high jumps on the first two phrases and long jumps on
   the third and fourth.

3. Try hopping on one foot and then on the other.

65

Nice Little Dog

Words by Libby Ann Martin — Traditional Tune

TENDERLY

The Camel

Words and Music by Cecilia Johns

RATHER SLOWLY BUT NOT DRAGGED

Up, down! Up, down! Up, down! Up, down! The cam - el walks in a fun - ny way,

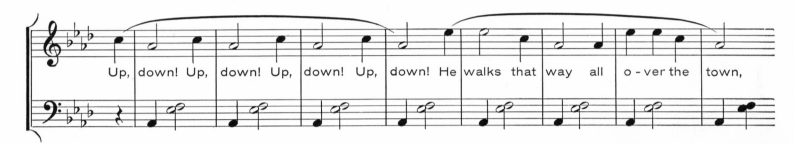

Up, down! Up, down! Up, down! Up, down! He walks that way all o - ver the town,

Up, down! Up, down! Up, down! Up, down!

One of the children may play "Up, down!" on these notes throughout the song:
C Ab

Two or three children may play "Up, down!" on these notes at different places on the keyboard, low or high.

The entire song may be played by using only these three notes:
Eb C Ab

One or two children may play this chord on the first beat of every measure:
C Ab

67

The Pony

Words and Music by Cecilia Johns

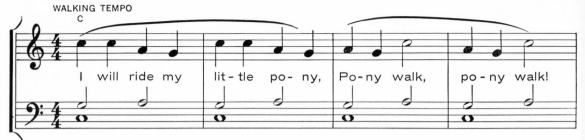

WALKING TEMPO
C

I will ride my lit-tle po-ny, Po-ny walk, po-ny walk!

F G7 C

I will ride my lit-tle po-ny all day long.

moderately 2. Pony trot! fast 3. Pony run! Play C (first note) in rhythm throughout.

Tippy

Words by Cynthia Putnam Music by Robert Pace

WITH HUMOR

Tip-py, the squir-rel, came down from his tree,

Try big and little leaps for this song.

But Tip-py went back when he saw me.

Chant for Creative Play

The Squirrel

Whisky, frisky,
Hippity hop,
Up he goes
To the tall tree top!

Whirly, twirly,
Round and round,
Down he scampers
To the ground.

Ancona Chicken

Words by Daniel Hooley   Adapted Folk Tune

WITH HUMOR

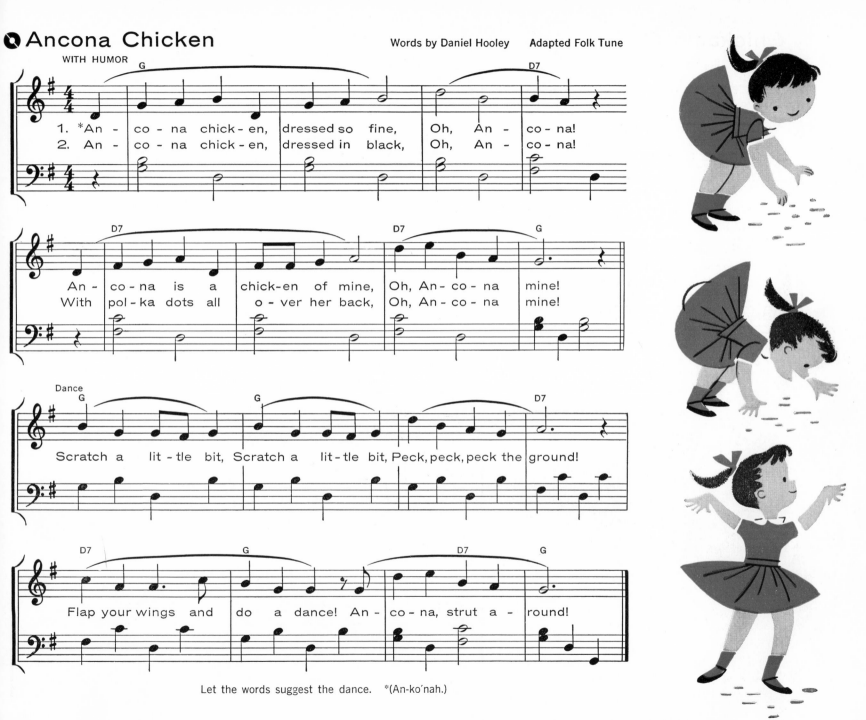

1. *An - co - na chick - en, dressed so fine, Oh, An - co - na!
2. An - co - na chick - en, dressed in black, Oh, An - co - na!

An - co - na is a chick-en of mine, Oh, An - co - na mine!
With pol - ka dots all o - ver her back, Oh, An - co - na mine!

Dance

Scratch a lit - tle bit, Scratch a lit - tle bit, Peck, peck, peck the ground!

Flap your wings and do a dance! An - co - na, strut a - round!

Let the words suggest the dance.   *(An-ko'nah.)

Chickama Craney Crow

Southern Folk Song

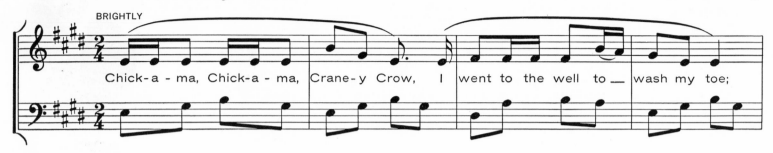

Chick-a-ma, Chick-a-ma, Crane-y Crow, I went to the well to _ wash my toe;

When I came home, one chick-en was gone! Oh, Chick-a-ma, Chick-a-ma Crane-y Crow!

Let sticks play the rhythm of "Chickama, Chickama, Craney Crow."

Parakeet

Words by Susan Rupert   Music by Daniel Hooley

1. Where are you hid-ing, par-a-keet?

Peep!   Peep!   Peep, peep, peep!

2. Oh, would you like a seed to eat?
   Peep! Peep! Peep, peep, peep!

3. Fly to my shoulder, parakeet!
   Peep! Peep! Peep, peep, peep!

70

Little Redbird

Words by Rebecca Stevens   American Folk Tune

HAPPILY

Lit - tle red-bird in the tree, Pass the hap-py news a - long,

Sang a song so cheer-i - ly, Pass the hap-py news a - long;

Pass the hap - py news a-long, Lis-ten to the red-bird's song:

Spring is com-ing, win-ter's done! Pass the hap-py news a - long.

Sing the last two measures three times, if you like.

71

Bees

Adapted Words   German Folk Tune

2. Hum, zum, zum,
   How the bees do hum!
   Busy bees must gather honey
   While the days are bright and
      sunny.
   Hum, zum, zum,
   How the bees do hum!

Let the children try hum-
ming or zumming the melody.

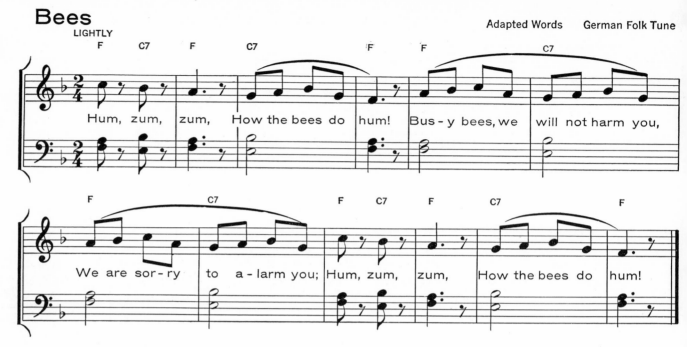

☉ Mr. Cricket

Words by Anita Alexander   Music by Roger Elston

2. Mister Cricket, will you dance
      for me?
   Dance! Dance! Dance!

3. Mister Cricket, will you jump
      for me?
   Jump! Jump! Jump!

4. Mister Robin, will you hop
      for me?
   Hop! Hop! Hop!

5. Mister Bullfrog, will you
      croak for me?
   Croak! Croak! Croak!

6. Mister Rabbit, will you run
      for me?
   Run! Run! Run!

Let the children think of
additional stanzas.

72

Butterflies

Words and Music by Richard C. Berg

FLOWINGLY

But - ter-flies in sum - mer make a pret - ty sight;

Some wear bright col - ors, some have wings of white.

Guppies

Words and Music by Robert Pace

WITH A SWING

Gup - pies and mol - lies and glit - ter - ing gold - fish,

They're all so small that they can - not be old fish.

Eency Weency Spider

Old Rhyme   American Tune

Een - cy ween-cy spi - der went up the wa - ter spout,

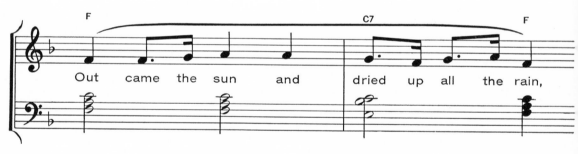

Down came the rain and washed the spi - der out;

Out came the sun and dried up all the rain,

And een - cy ween-cy spi - der went up the spout a-gain.

74

Flip-Flop

Words by Jean Hoover   Music by Eleanor Vaught

WELL ACCENTED

With a flip - flop here, And a flip - flop there, The fish is out of the wa - ter;____

With a swish-swash here, And a swish-swash there, The fish flips back in the wa-ter.

Baby Alligator

Words and Music by First-grade Children

SIMPLY

I'm a ba - by al - li - ga - tor, Just a lit - tle one, I like to float in

wa - ter deep And lie in the sun, And sleep and sleep and sleep.____

slower

75

SONGS FOR RHYTHM BAND

The Triangle

Words and Music by Robert Pace

HAPPILY

Ring, ring, ring ting - a - ling! Ring, ring, ring ting - a - ling!

Ring, ring, ring ting - a - ling! I'll make the tri - an - gle sing ting - a - ling!

Rhythm Sticks

NOT FAST

1. Sticks go click click, Hear them click click; Sticks go click click, keep-ing time.

2. Click-a-click-click,
Click-a-click-click,
Click-a-click-click,
Keeping time.

Tambourine

LIGHTLY

Tap, tap and shake, Tap, tap and shake! Two kinds of sounds the tam-bou-rines make.

Cymbals

HAPPILY

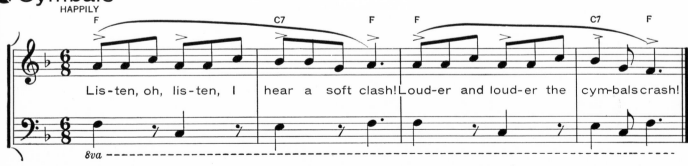

Lis-ten, oh, lis-ten, I hear a soft clash! Loud-er and loud-er the cym-bals crash!

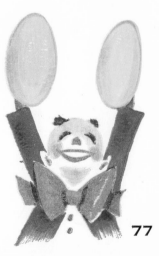

77

Jingle Sticks

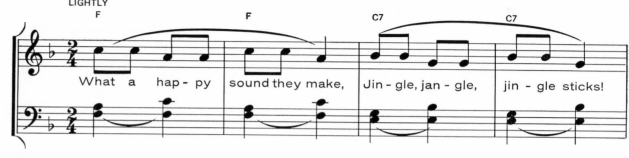

LIGHTLY

What a hap - py sound they make, Jin - gle, jan - gle, jin - gle sticks!

Lis - ten, lis - ten as we shake Jin - gle, jan - gle, jin - gle sticks.

Drum

VIGOROUSLY

Drum, drum, rum - ty - tum! Beat the drum a rum - ty - tum!

Drum, drum, rum - ty - tum! Rum - ty tum, the drum!

Wood Block

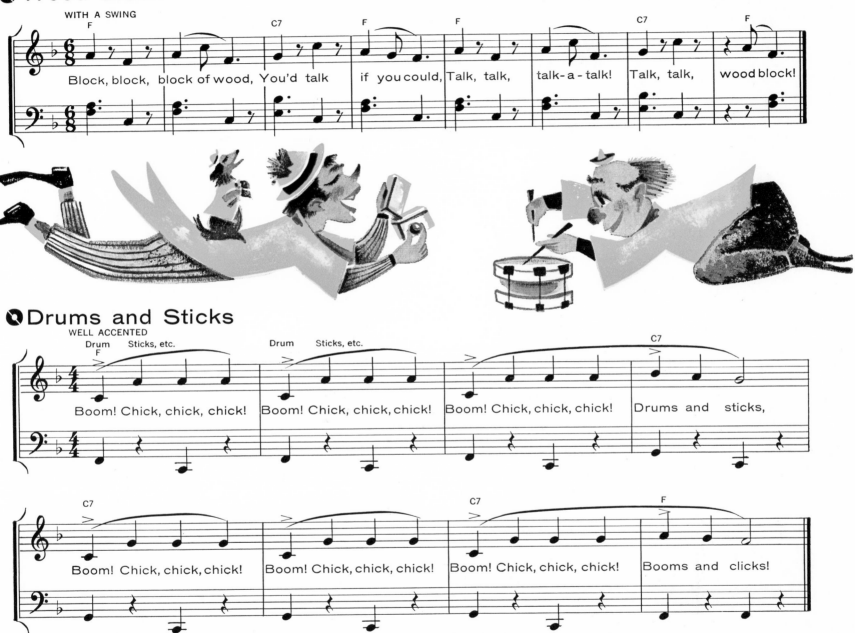

WITH A SWING

Block, block, block of wood, You'd talk if you could, Talk, talk, talk-a-talk! Talk, talk, wood block!

Drums and Sticks

WELL ACCENTED

Drum   Sticks, etc.   Drum   Sticks, etc.

Boom! Chick, chick, chick! Boom! Chick, chick, chick! Boom! Chick, chick, chick! Drums and sticks,

Boom! Chick, chick, chick! Boom! Chick, chick, chick! Boom! Chick, chick, chick! Booms and clicks!

When the drum beats, the sticks play an imaginary beat in the air. The sticks are played together on "Chick, chick, chick!"

Go In and Out the Windows

English Folk Game

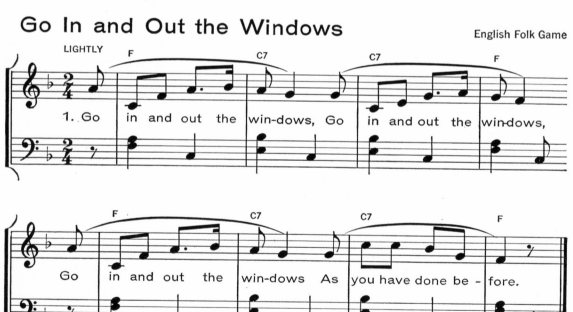

1. Go in and out the win-dows, Go in and out the win-dows,
Go in and out the win-dows As you have done be - fore.

2. Now stand and face your partner, etc.
3. Now follow him (her) to London, etc.
4. Now shake his (her) hands and leave him (her), etc.

Shoo, Fly!

Early American Singing Game

WITH GOOD HUMOR

Shoo, fly, don't both-er me! Shoo, fly, don't both-er me! Shoo, fly, don't both-er me!

I'm ex-pect-ing com-pa-ny. I feel, I feel, I feel, I feel like the morn-ing star;

I feel, I feel, I feel, I feel like the morn-ing star.

Pease Porridge

Mother Goose   Traditional Tune

SIMPLY

1. Pease por-ridge hot, pease por-ridge cold, Pease por-ridge in the pot nine days old.
2. Some like it hot, some like it cold, I like it in the pot nine days old.

Great A

Mother Goose   Music by Florence Waite

HUMOROUSLY

Great A, lit - tle a, bounc-ing B, The cat's in the cup-board and can't see me!

Three Blind Mice

Mother Goose   Traditional Tune

BRIGHTLY

Three blind mice, — Three blind mice, — See how they run! — See how they run! —

They all ran aft-er the far-mer's wife, She cut off their tails with a carv-ing knife,

Did ev - er you see such a sight in your life as three blind mice? —

Looby Loo

English Singing Game

WITH A SWING

Here we go loo-by loo,
Here we go loo-by light,
Here we go loo-by loo,
All on a Sat-ur-day night. —

I put my right hand in, — I take my right hand out, —

Go to the beginning

I give my hand a shake, shake, shake, And turn my-self a-bout. Oh,

2. left hand. 3. right foot 4. left foot 5. big head 6. whole self

The children form a circle and go through the motions described in the song.

83

The Bear Went Over the Mountain

Popular Song

QUICKLY AND LIGHTLY

Oh, the bear went o-ver the moun-tain, The bear went o-ver the moun-tain,

The bear went o-ver the moun-tain To see what he could see; ___

And all that he could see, ___ And all that he could see ___

Was the oth-er side of the moun-tain, The oth-er side of the moun-tain;

84

The oth-er side of the moun-tain Was all that he could see. ___

Round the Mountain

Old American Song

GAILY

1. She'll be com-ing round the moun-tain when she comes, ___ She'll be com-ing round the

moun-tain when she comes, ___ She'll be com-ing round the moun-tain, She'll be

com-ing round the moun-tain, She'll be com-ing round the moun-tain when she comes. ___

2. She'll be driving six white horses when she comes, etc.
3. We will kill the old red rooster when she comes, etc.
4. Oh, we'll all have chicken and dumplings when she comes, etc.
What else might we all have? "choc'late candy"? "cake and ice cream"?

85

Sing a Song of Sixpence

Mother Goose   Music by J. W. Elliott

FREELY
Play sticks ♪. ♪ throughout

Sing a song of six-pence, a pock-et full of rye,

Four and twen-ty black-birds baked in a pie;

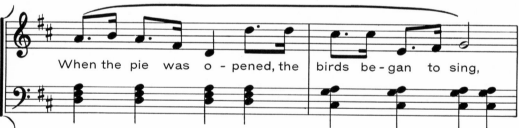

When the pie was o-pened, the birds be-gan to sing,

Was-n't that a dain-ty dish to set be-fore the king?

Encourage the children to try all kinds of skips to this music:
high, low, soft, cross-legged. Let them skip fast and slow.

86

To Market

WITH AN EASY SWING

Mother Goose   Traditional Tune

1. To mar-ket, to mar-ket, to buy a fine pig; Home a-gain, home a-gain, jig-ge-ty jig!
2. To mar-ket, to mar-ket, to buy a fine hog; Home a-gain, home a-gain, jig-ge-ty jog!

Children enjoy these activities:

1. Walk to and from the market.
2. Walk to the market. Carry a heavy load home.
3. Skip to and from the market.
4. Skip to the market and walk home.

A-Hunting We Will Go

BRIGHTLY

English Folk Song

1. Oh, a - hunt-ing we will go, a - hunt-ing we will go;

We'll catch a lit - tle fox and put him in a box and then we'll let him. go.

2. We'll catch a little squirrel and give it to a girl.
3. We'll catch a little dog and put it on a log.
4. We'll catch a little fish and put it in a dish.
5. We'll catch a little mouse and take it in the house.
6. We'll catch a little pig and make it do a jig.

Can your children think up additional stanzas?

87

Skip to My Lou

American Singing Game

The children choose partners and skip in a circle.

All Around the Maypole

American Singing Game

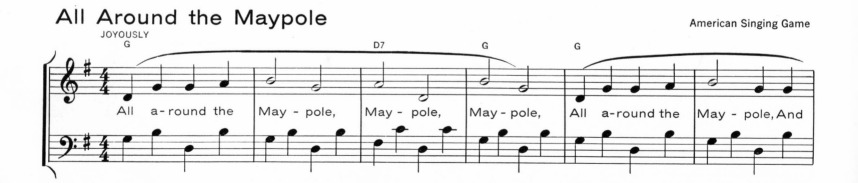

now, Miss Sal-ly, won't you dance for joy? | Dance for joy, | dance for joy, | dance for joy!

Clap to the end

And | now, Miss Sal-ly, won't you | dance for joy? And | now, Miss Sal-ly, won't you | bow?

The children join hands and form a circle around a child standing in the center. The child is "Miss Sally." All walk around singing until they begin to clap for Miss Sally, who dances. When Miss Sally bows, she bows in front of a child, who then takes her place.

Miss Sally may jump for joy, skip for joy, or make any other motions she pleases.

Goosey Gander

Mother Goose   Music by Florence Waite

IN FOUR-MEASURE PHRASES

Goos-ey Goos-ey | Gan - der, | night-cap on his | head,

Turns him-self and | twists him-self and | then he goes to | bed.

89

Green Gravel

English Folk Song

WITH A LILT

Green grav-el, green grav-el, the grass is so green For the {brav-est young / pret-ti-est} fel-low / fair maid that ev-er was seen; We'll wash {him / her} in milk, and we'll dress {him / her} in pink, And write down {his / her} name with a gold pen and ink.

Green Peas

Southern Folk Game

NOT FAST

Oh, green peas! Bless my soul! Tell me whom you choose, Bless my soul!

*Jimmy Smith, your name is called; Come take a seat right beside the wall!

Shake his hand and let him go because he won't sit in the chair anymore.

*Call the name of someone who is present.

Seesaw, Margery Daw

Mother Goose   Music by J. W. Elliott

WITH AN EASY SWING

See - saw, Mar-ger-y Daw, Jack shall have a new mas - ter,

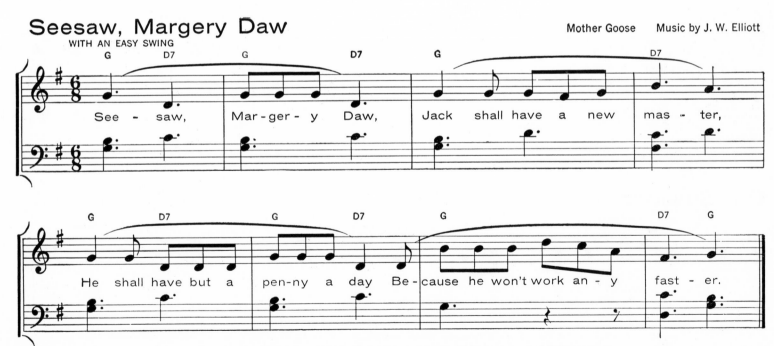

He shall have but a pen-ny a day Be-cause he won't work an-y fast - er.

Big swings and little swings may be made to this music; and big seesaws and little seesaws.

Yankee Doodle

Words by Dr. Shackburg   Early American Tune

Yan-kee Doo-dle came to town, A - rid-ing on a po - ny, He stuck a feath-er in his cap And called it mac-a - ro - ni. Yan - kee Doo-dle, keep it up, Yan - kee Doo-dle dan - dy, Mind the mu-sic and the step, And with the girls be hand-y.

Oh! Susanna

Words and Music by Stephen Foster

I come from A - la - bam - a with my ban-jo on my knee, I'm going to Lou-'si -

an - a, my | true love for to see. | Oh, Su - san-na, oh, don't you cry for me,

For I'm | going to Lou - 'si - | an - a | with | my | ban - jo on my | knee.

Crosspatch

Old Rhyme   Music by Florence Waite

WITH MOCK ADMONITION

Cross-patch, | draw the latch, | Sit by the fire and spin;

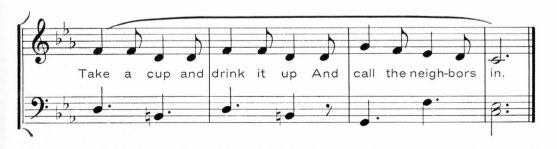

Take a cup and | drink it up And | call the neigh-bors in.

Barber, Barber

Mother Goose Traditional Tune

WITH HUMOR

"Bar-ber, bar-ber, shave a pig! How man-y hairs will make a wig?"

"Four and twen-ty, that's e-nough!" Give the bar-ber a pinch of snuff.

Handy Pandy

Mother Goose Music by Robert Pace

GAILY

Han-dy pan-dy, Jack-a-dan-dy Loves plum cake and sug-ar can-dy;

He bought some at a gro-cer's shop, And out he came, hop, hop, hop!

Barcarolle

Robert Pace

The piano compositions may be used for many different activities if you vary the tempos and dynamics of each piece. For example, at a moderate tempo, "Promenade" (page 99) depicts quiet motions; a slower tempo suggests a leisurely walk; and a rapid tempo indicates the excitement of a running movement. Changes of dynamics from loud to soft and from soft to loud as well as corresponding changes of tempo add further possibilities for creative movement.

A Slow Chant for Creative Movement
Sit on a seesaw and ride up on high!
Come back to earth with a bump!
Every ride that you take to the sky
Means a ride back to earth with a bump!

Waltz

Swing and sway to the waltz. Bend to it, and turn to it. Bells, triangles, and sticks may play along with the piano.

Daniel Hooley

Rhythmic Theme in F

Robert Pace

A Chant for Creative Movement

The merry-go-round goes up and down,
The merry-go-round goes 'round and 'round;
Up! Down! Around, around!
On the merry-go-round!

This music suggests many different kinds of movements: galloping like horses on a merry-go-round; high, low, big, and little skips; walking; hopping; and jumping.

You can also use rhythm instruments with the selection.

96

Gigue

Robert Pace

"Chorale" is excellent for the rest period and quiet listening. Occasionally a slow walk to it appeals to the children.

Chorale

Florence Waite

Theme

Roger Elston

Try tiptoeing to "Theme." Try, also, light running steps. Bells, shakers, and the triangle may play along.

Little Study

Daniel Hooley

A. Run forward.   B. Run in a circle.   A. Run in place.   The children may like to tiptoe to this music. They may also clap or tap to it.

Promenade

Robert Pace

slow   Walk through snow or sand.
crisply   Walk on a very hot sidewalk.

Try various other ways to walk; like a policeman, for instance, or a giant. Walk in a hurry. Walk in a wedding procession.

A Chant for Stepping

Step, step, step, step,
Lift your knees,
If you please!
Step, step, step, step,
Stepping up and down.

A Chant for Stepping and Hopping

One, two, buckle my shoe;
Three, four, shut the door;
Five, six, pick up sticks;
Seven, eight, lay them straight;
Nine, ten, a good fat hen.

Chordal Theme

Robert Pace

A Chant for Walking

Walking, walking down the street;
Smile at everyone you meet;
Walking, walking down the street;
Stop!

Looking, looking up and down;
Streets are busy in our town;
Look to the left! Look to the right!
Cross!

Walking, walking down the street;
Smile at everyone you meet;
Walking, walking down the street;
Home!

Happy Days

Daniel Hooley

Staccato throughout

Start playing slowly and increase in speed in the first 8 measures. Do the same for the second 8 measures and then for the repeat. Sticks may do a tick-tock beat throughout the piece.

The children may walk in various ways, tiptoe, or step to the music.

At a Picnic

W. A. Mozart

If the picnic is in the country, the children may walk, play ball, and swim to the music.
If the picnic is in a city park, they may swing, seesaw, ride the merry-go-round, and go wading in the pool.

Marching

Robert Pace

Continue staccato throughout

Start marching far away, approach, and pass by.

Folk Theme

Daniel Hooley

A

End

B

Go to the beginning

This is a good selection for stepping, galloping, skipping, and hopping.

A   Skip or hop.
B   Turn and skip or hop in the opposite direction.
A   Turn and skip or hop in the original direction.

Jump like a cricket, a kangaroo, a frog, and a rabbit.

A Chant for Leaping, Jumping, and Hopping

> Jump! Jump!
> Jump up and down!
> Jump! Jump!
> All over town!

Jump! Jump!
Jump up high!
Jump! Jump!
To the sky!

Jump! Jump!
Jump to the side!
Jump! Jump!
Make it wide!

By substituting other words for "jump" (hop, skip, dance, etc.), the children may improvise verses for this chant.

Impromptu

Robert Pace

A Dance

Robert Pace

"A Dance" may be used in many ways to help develop a feeling for pulse. The children may swing, sway, play seesaw, and play elephant to it. Or they may be swinging bells, the pendulum of a clock, or trees swaying in the breeze. They may play the drum, sticks, and triangle on the first beat of every measure.

A Chant for Creative Movement

A kite can go up, up, up!
A kite can go down, down, down!
A kite can be caught by the wind
And go 'round and 'round and 'round!

Indian Dance

Robert Pace

It is fun to use tom-toms, sticks, and shakers with this dance.

Ecossaise

Franz Schubert

FAST

Use "Ecossaise" for turning and twisting. It is also a good selection for the use of rhythm instruments

Waltz in E Flat

Florence Waite

Swing and sway to the music.

Country Dance

Ludwig van Beethoven

Try just one movement for this dance. Then try two movements: slow and fast.
Play the first 4 measures slowly, the next 4 measures fast, etc. You can also try changing
the levels of movement, from low to high. Change, too, from heavy to light movements.

A Fairy Tale

Dmitri Kabalevsky

pp Once upon a time.. cresc.

Make up your own fairy tale. ("Once upon a time there was a little...”). Let the music help tell the story.

Andante Cantabile

J. C. Bach

SIMPLY

Let the children make up their own movements for this selection and for "Little Piece," which follows.

Little Piece

Robert Schumann

♪ Happy Birthday

Traditional Song

GAILY

Just six years old to-day,   Just six years old to-day!
(seven)   (seven)

Hap-py Birth-day!   Hap-py Birth-day!   Jim-my's six years old to - day.
(seven)

Today's My Birthday

Words and Music by Richard C. Berg

How old are you? How old are you? I'm six years old to - day.
(seven)

Witches

Words and Music by Richard C. Berg

I know there are no witch-es that go rid-ing through the air,

But I pre-tend at Hal-low-een that they are real-ly there!

The children might like to sing a neutral syllable (loo, woo, boo) as a second stanza while they interpret the face, the walk, and the gestures of witches to the rhythm of the music.

111

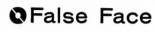 False Face

Words by Susan Rupert   Music by David Russell

GLEEFULLY

Who's be-hind this false face? No-bod-y knows but me! Who's be-hind this false face?

No-bod-y knows but me! I won't tell you, You will have to guess;

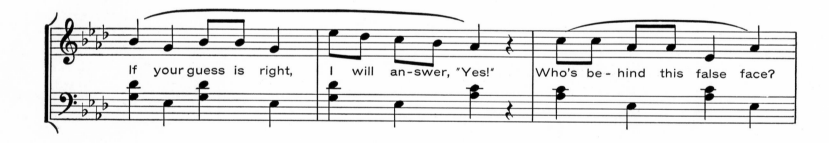

If your guess is right, I will an-swer, "Yes!" Who's be-hind this false face?

No-bod-y knows but me! Who's be-hind this false face? No-bod-y knows but me!

Halloween Pumpkin

Words by Mary Francis   Music by Elsie Smith

MODERATELY

Scoop out the in-side of a pump-kin, Make a mouth, a nose, and two big eyes;

Put a light in-side the pump-kin, And you'll have a Hal-low-een sur-prise.

Goblin in the Dark

Words by Agnes Webster   Old Tune

MYSTERIOUSLY

1. The gob-lin in the dark, the gob-lin in the dark!

Hi! Ho! On Hal-low-een, the gob-lin in the dark.

The tune of this song is "The Farmer in the Dell" in a minor key. The game is played in the same way as the original song. Form a circle with one child in the center who is the "goblin."

2. The goblin calls a witch, etc.
3. The witch calls a bat, etc.
4. The bat calls a "ghost," etc.
5. The ghost says, "Boo!", etc.
6. They all scream and screech, etc.

113

Halloween Night

SCARILY

Words by Lou Ann Hatcher   Music by Mary Riccio

Witch-es and gob-lins, Jack-o'-lan-terns and fun-ny fac-es!

Black cats and fly-ing bats Come on Hal-low-een night! Boo!

A Song of Thanks

Traditional Hymn

SIMPLY

Thank You for the world so sweet; Thank You for the food we eat;

Thank You for the birds that sing; Thank You, God, for ev-'ry-thing.

114

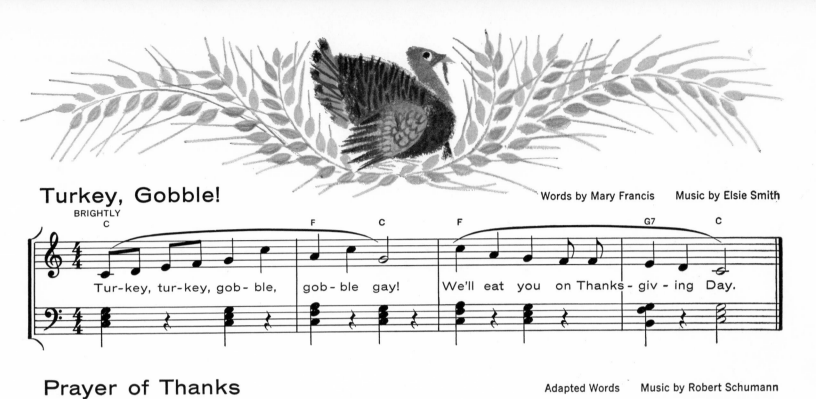

Turkey, Gobble!

Words by Mary Francis   Music by Elsie Smith

BRIGHTLY

Tur-key, tur-key, gob-ble, gob-ble gay! We'll eat you on Thanks-giv-ing Day.

Prayer of Thanks

Adapted Words   Music by Robert Schumann

DEVOUTLY

1. Thank you, Fa-ther, for our par-ents; Thank you, Fa-ther, for our homes.
2. Thank you, for our friends and neigh-bors; Help us to be kind and good.

Prayer

Traditional Hymn

SLOWLY, WITH REVERENCE

Let us with a joy-ful mind Praise the Lord, for He is kind.

Santa Claus Is Coming

Words by Jean Hoover   Music by Robert Pace

Ringle jingle, ringle jingle, Santa's on his way, Ringle jingle, ringle jingle, coming in his sleigh; Ringle jingle, ringle jingle, Santa Claus is near, Ringle jingle, ringle jingle, Santa's almost here!

Christmas Is Coming

English Rhyme   Music by Edith Nesbit

Christmas is coming, The goose is getting fat, Please to put a penny in the

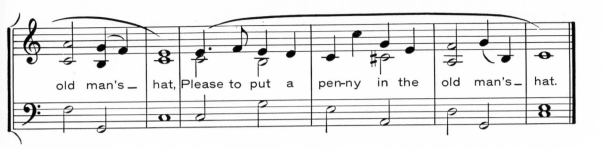

old man's — hat, Please to put a pen-ny in the old man's — hat.

O Christmas Tree

Words by Rebecca Stevens   Music by Anthony Burke

JOYOUSLY

O Christ-mas tree, O Christ-mas tree! How we love to see you!

We'll make some trim-mings just for you, Of red and gold and green and blue.

O Christ-mas tree, O Christ-mas tree! How we love to see you!

We Wish You a Merry Christmas

Old English Song

HAPPILY

We wish you a Mer-ry Christ-mas, We wish you a Mer-ry Christ-mas!

We wish you a Mer-ry Christ-mas and a Hap-py New Year!

Christmas Day

Adapted Words   Swedish Folk Tune

GAILY

Christ-mas Day will soon be here, and I can hard-ly wait; Christ-mas Day will

soon be here, and I can hard-ly wait; San-ta will be com-ing,

Soon he will be com - ing; Christ-mas Day will soon be here, and I can hard-ly wait!

Merry Christmas

Words and Music by Robert Pace

Mer-ry Christ-mas, Mer-ry Christ-mas and a Hap-py New Year! Come and join us, come and

join us in all the good cheer! Hear the car-ols, hear the car - ols ring-ing out on the air!

Mer-ry Christ-mas, Mer-ry Christ-mas and a Hap-py New Year!

119

A Valentine

Words by Rebecca Stevens   Music by Anthony Burke

EXPECTANTLY

1. What will be in the en-ve-lope? A val-en-tine for me, I hope.
2. What will it say on the val-en-tine? "I love you so, O please be mine!"

Abraham Lincoln

Words by Susan Rupert   Music by Daniel Hooley

FLOWINGLY

A-bra-ham Lin-coln, kind and good, Is hon-ored and

loved by man-y; To help us re-mem-ber this

Pres-i-dent, We put his face on our pen-ny.

Our Flag

Words and Music by First-grade Children

WITH SPIRIT

We pledge al - le - giance to our flag, Red, White, and Blue,

And to the Re - pub - lic for which it stands! Red, White, and Blue!

Glory to the Flag

Adapted from "The Battle Hymn of the Republic"

1. Glo - ry, glo - ry, hal - le - lu - iah! Our own Red, White, and Blue!

2. Glory, glory, halleluiah!
   We all salute our flag.

3. Glory, glory, halleluiah!
   We love our country's flag.

121

George Washington

Words and Music by David Russell

SIMPLY

There's some-thing a-bout George Wash-ing-ton You should know;

He was our ver-y first Pres-i-dent, Man-y years a-go.

Easter Bunny

Words by Anne Beyer   Music by Daniel Hooley

LIGHTLY

Friend-ly East-er Bun-ny is bus-y as can be,

He's col-or-ing eggs and mak-ing bas-kets for you and me.

122

Easter Bunny's Coming

Words by Marianne St. John   Music by David Russell

WITH A SWING

1. The East - er Bun - ny's com - ing, com - ing, com - ing!

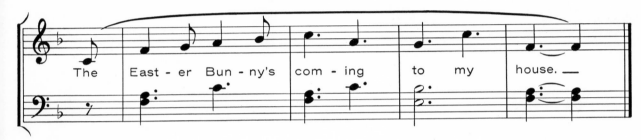

The East - er Bun - ny's com - ing to my house.

2. He'll come when I am sleeping, sleeping, sleeping,
   He'll come when I am sleeping in my bed.

3. He'll leave an Easter basket, basket, basket,
   He'll leave an Easter basket just for me.

4. I'll find some colored eggs and Easter candy,
   I'll find some eggs and candy just for me!

   Let the children hop like Easter bunnies to this song.

Easter Treats

Words by Julie Gibault   Music by Robert Pace

SIMPLY

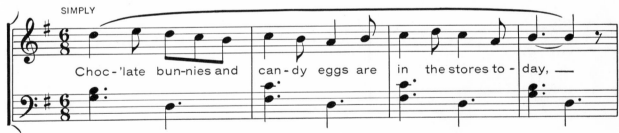

Choc - 'late bun - nies and can - dy eggs are in the stores to - day, ___

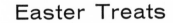

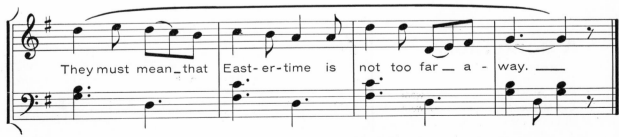

They must mean __ that East - er - time is not too far - a - way. ___

Old MacDonald's Farm

MODERATELY

Old Mac Don-ald had a farm, E - I - E - I - O,

And on this farm he had some chick-ens, E - I - E - I - O.

A Song Story

Based on Folk Melodies

Some boys and girls from the city went to visit Old MacDonald's Farm. They went first of all to see the chickens.

124

CHICKENS

NOT FAST

G

All a-round the barn-yard, barn-yard, barn-yard,

G   **D7**   **G**

All a-round the barn-yard, scratch-ing up corn!

G

All a-round the barn-yard, barn-yard, barn-yard,

G   **D7**   **G**

All a-round the barn-yard, sure's you're born!

Next, they saw six white ducks waddling across the barnyard.

SIX WHITE DUCKS

WITH A BOUNCE

There were six white ducks which once I knew, ___ Fat ducks, pret-ty ducks they were, too;

But the one with the feath-ers rolled up on his back, He ruled the oth-ers with a "Quack, quack, quack!"

Then, out of the barn came a proud old tom turkey.

MISTER TURKEY

WITH A SLOW STRUT

Who's that strut-ting 'round look-ing might-y perk-y? Looks like it might be old Mis-ter Tur-key.

Strut, Mis - ter Tur-key! That's a fan-cy way to walk.

Strut, Mis - ter Tur-key! That's a fan-cy way to walk.

Then they watched four little pigs playing and eating.

FOUR LITTLE PIGS

NOT FAST

Way down yon-der where the sun sets red, Four lit-tle pig-gies eat-ing good corn bread,

Corn bread and cab-bage fit for a king, But four lit-tle pig-gies will eat an-y old thing.

Before they left the farm, the children sang a song about Old MacDonald's Farm. The animals helped them sing it:

127

*2. ducks, quack
3. turkeys, gobble
4. pigs, oink

128

Squeaker at the Zoo

MODERATELY

Go-ing to the zoo, Go-ing to the zoo! The sun is bright, the sky is blue; Squeak-er, you may come a-long too. Go-ing to the zoo, Go-ing to the zoo!

A Song Story

Words and Music by Daniel Hooley

Some boys and girls went to visit the zoo. Their dog, Squeaker, went with them. He liked to visit the animals, too. As the children walked along, they sang "Going to the Zoo."

The boys and girls went to see the animals they liked best. They saw the ostrich, the kangaroo, the leopard, and many other animals. While they were watching the camels, they discovered that Squeaker was not with them. Where could he be? Had they lost him?

129

SADLY

Oh, where, oh, where has my lit-tle dog gone? Oh, where, oh, where can he be?

With his tail cut short and his ears cut long, Oh, where, oh, where can he be? ___

They hurried to their friends, the elephants, and asked them:

NOT FAST

Have you seen a lit-tle dog with a coat of white and tan?

His tail is short, and his ears go flop! Please help us, if you can.

130

The elephants answered:

RHYTHMICALLY

No, no, no, no, no, no, no, no! We wave our trunks to and fro;

No, no, no, no, no, no, no, no! We have-n't seen your dog.

They ran to the cage of the lions to see if the lions had seen Squeaker.

NOT FAST

Have you seen a lit-tle dog with a coat of white and tan?

His tail is short, and his ears go flop! Please help us, if you can.

131

The lions answered:

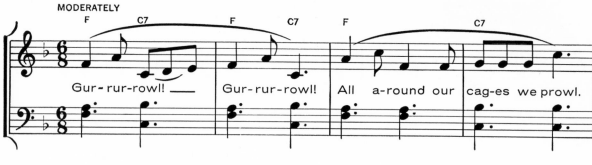

Gur-rur-rowl! ___ Gur-rur-rowl! All a-round our cag-es we prowl.

Gur-rur-rowl! ___ Gur-rur-rowl! We have-n't seen your dog.

Some of the children thought the hyenas might know where Squeaker was. So they went to ask the hyenas. They found them laughing as usual, but they stopped long enough for the children to ask:

Have you seen a lit-tle dog with a coat of white and tan?

His tail is short, and his ears go flop! Please help us, if you can.

The hyenas answered:

WELL ACCENTED

No, no, no! Ha-ha, ho-ho! We hold our sides 'cause we're laugh-ing so;

No, no, no! Ha-ha, ho-ho! We have-n't seen your dog.

Then the boys and girls went to see the giraffes. They asked the big, long-necked animals about Squeaker.

NOT FAST

Have you seen a lit-tle dog with a coat of white and tan?

His tail is short, and his ears go flop! Please help us, if you can.

133

The giraffes said:

RATHER SLOWLY, WITH DIGNITY

Our necks are so long that we can see all o-ver the park and the zoo;

We see your dog by the brown bear's cage, He's wait-ing there for you.

So the boys and girls went straight to the brown bear's cage and found the little dog, Squeaker. He was glad to see them, and they were happy that they had found him.

As they walked back home, they sang this song:

BRIGHTLY

Go-ing home from the zoo, Go-ing home from the zoo! The sun is bright, the sky is blue;

Our dog, Squeak-er, is with us, too! Go-ing home from the zoo, Go-ing home from the zoo!

MUSIC EDUCATION IN THE KINDERGARTEN

What is a music program for kindergarten?

To be satisfactory, a music program for kindergarten should furnish the child with a wide variety of musical experiences through which he can fully express and enjoy himself. It should include not only singing and games but also playing on rhythm instruments and simple melody instruments, improvising free movements, creating verses and even little tunes, dancing, and listening. It should, furthermore, help him to develop and express the pulses and moods of such music as is within the comprehension of five- and six-year-old minds and emotions. It is an "arts" program, not a "play" program. At first glance, such a program seems too complicated. In reality, however, it is not, for all its parts can be brought together and combined, as in this book and the recordings which accompany it. Here, some 200 songs and instrumental pieces are supplied, through which each child can express himself and gain a sense of individual achievement.

But his expression must not be divided into separate categories with, say, one song for singing, another for listening, and still another for physical activity. Each song in this book may be used for a variety of expressions. Take, for instance, "Lady, Lady!" on page 18. How can it be used to greatest advantage for both musical experience and educational growth? Children like the idea in the text and find the tune and verses delightful to sing. They may sing the song softly as a lullaby. They may sing it a little faster as a dance tune, and dance to it in free movement. They may use a triangle to accompany the singing, or play just two notes throughout the song on bells or the piano if one is available. They may hear it played as a lullaby, for relaxation in quiet listening. These various activities, combining a variety of music experiences, are noted in the suggestions printed on the page on which the song appears.

Or take "A Fish Story" on page 8. Not only is the tune very singable, but the verses are amusing to the child and also help him to learn to count. The song gives him the experience of singing loudly or softly, high and low — *laying the foundation of a feeling for dynamics*. It allows him to experience the movement of the melody line as it ascends and descends — *laying the foundation for music-reading readiness* later on in his musical education. The child may also use rhythm instruments to accompany the song — *experiencing the pulse in music*.

How the child "explores" music

Such suggestions as those just cited accompany many of the songs in this book. We urge you not to confine yourself to following them but to invent new ways of experiencing songs and to encourage your children to do so too. As can readily be seen, these varied music activities are made up largely of exploratory experiences for the child. Just as he "explores" in language, experimenting with his word vocabulary, testing a word and using it many times during the day because he likes it and is pleased and proud that he has learned it, so should he be encouraged to "explore" music. The understanding teacher who provides the child with the proper atmosphere and the privilege of being creative and constantly *curious* about the music materials around him is furnishing him with the field for his exploration.

Of course, she does not allow "activities" to rob him of good tone quality and expressive singing, but she realizes that singing does not comprise the whole of the music program. In addition to *singing with good tone*, the child in his explorations in the music field needs time to *dance freely to the song*, to *play its rhythm* on a drum or wood block, to *play portions of it* on bells or the piano, to *make up verses to it*, to *listen actively* if it is played on a record player or the piano. He needs not merely to *hear high and low tones* but also to *express them* in bodily movement or on the drum or wood block. He needs time to *make his own high and low tones* on the piano or bells. He needs to hear someone else's idea of correct pitch, desirable tone, and appropriate degree of loudness or softness. Learning at first by imitation, he will soon make the skill or the idea his own by manipulating what he hears to fit what he wants to say musically.

One of the most pleasing and rewarding exploratory experiences for children has to do with melody bells. They may be introduced very early because they require no finger dexterity. The child simply handles a little mallet. In the beginning, he needs time and freedom to find out *for himself* that the longer bars have the lower voices. Sometimes it is wise to begin by suspending the bell set so that *low* is physically low and *high* is physically high. But in a very short time the child makes the adjustment toward an understanding that when the bells are flat on the table, *low* is on the left and *high* is on the right. Exploring the song "Six Little Apples" on page 3, for instance, will lead him to hear and to manipulate *high high low*. Or you may prefer to use resonator bells, with

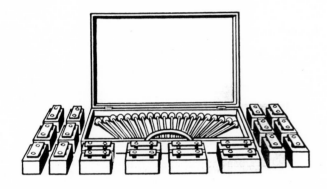

each bar mounted on its own resonator block. They can be moved about readily and grouped as needed. It is also desirable to have

a piano in the room, so that the child may experiment with the keyboard, locating and sounding high and low notes, loud and soft notes, in somewhat the same manner as he explores the melody or resonator bells.

If you are patient and imaginative as he explores the music field, the child will learn to express himself musically with satisfaction equal to his satisfaction in expressing himself in words. He will be pleased with his progress and want to continue growing musically. As the year passes, you will find that the child

knows and enjoys more songs.

has better control of his singing voice.

has developed better muscular coordination.

has a better sense of rhythm.

moves freely to music.

can handle rhythm instruments more successfully.

has developed a greater creativity.

makes up songs or additional verses to songs.

makes up dances.

acts out, or dramatizes, songs and song stories.

can play tones on the keyboard.

evinces a greater interest in music activities.

Periodically, you may want to ask the children some such question as, "What have we learned about songs?" If you have provided a happy field for exploration, you may expect to hear from the children, in their own words or movements, that songs

may be fast or slow.

may be medium fast or medium slow.

may be loud or soft or somewhere in-between.

may begin high or low.

may end high or low.

can tell how you feel: happy, sad, funny, gay, spooky, and the like.

So great an accomplishment in their early exploration in music is indeed encouraging to the children and satisfying to any teacher in her efforts to help them in their emotional and mental growth. She may be sure she has laid for them a good foundation in music education.

Some encouraging points to remember

In case your confidence begins to falter when you consider the scope of the music program and its far-reaching effects, here are a few points to remember:

The untrained voice is more acceptable to children than the trained voice of an opera singer.

You know your children better than does anyone else in the school.

Feel free to explore and to improvise with your children.

Learn how to capitalize upon the suggestions and guidance of the music specialist or consultant.

Children will be as good or as bad as you permit them to be.

Demand as high standards as are compatible with the development and age of the children.

Use a pitch pipe, piano, or bells as checks regarding pitch.

Learn your own vocal range and check it against that of your children. If the two are approximately the same, you may not have to rely a great deal upon a pitch pipe.

Use informal gestures which have rhythmic and musical significance in getting the children to sing and participate in activities. Do not use a rigid or fixed beat.

Use the piano as an *aid*. Let it reinforce, not dominate the singing.

Use the record player, too, as an *aid*. It can never replace the teacher, for it can only present the recorded version of the song, leaving a great deal of actual teaching to be done.

Don't underestimate your own ability to teach music, for there is no such person as a teacher who has no contribution to make to the music program. A little confidence plus the availability of the most modern materials will work miracles in the classroom.

What sort of songs are desirable for young children?

Various criteria should be applied to songs in determining whether they are suitable for five- and six-year-olds, for song content is perhaps the most important aspect in music education. These criteria involve (1) the text, its meaning and word imagery, (2) the rhythm and melody of the music, (3) mood, (4) tone quality and (5) creative implications.

1. The Text. The words in the verses should be familiar to the child, or easily explainable in terms of his own speaking vocabulary. Take, for instance, the song "Let Us Dance Together" on page 49. The stanza might have read:

> Listen to the music,
> Join the happy throng;
> Let us dance together
> As we sing a song.

But "throng" has no meaning for small children; it is not in their speaking vocabulary. The stanza, therefore, has been made to read:

> Listen to the music,
> What a happy sound!
> Let us sing together,
> As we dance around.

The ideas expressed and the words used to express them are familiar to the child.

Another example of good word usage is found in "O Christmas Tree," page 117. This wording might have been used:

> We'll make bright trimmings just for you
> Of green and gold and ev'ry hue.

To an adult, the lines call up a pleasing image of a gaily decked tree, but to a child they are confusing. "Hue" to him is most likely a boy's name! And "bright *trimmings*" is difficult for him to sing. So the lines are made to read:

> We'll make some trimmings just for you,
> Of red and gold and green and blue.

Here we have a vocabulary within the child's understanding and, as in all good songs for young children, vivid word images.

The child's own descriptive vocabulary is colorful and free from clichés. His songs should reflect this natural inclination of his. For example, in "Bumbershoot," page 37, "A plip-plop, a pitter pat" is more understandable to him and much more expressive than "The raindrops fall with a plip-plop sound." "Hopping his hoppity way to you" in "Hoppy, the Kangaroo," page 59, is more vivid and descriptive to the child than would be some such wording as "Hopping, he comes on his way to you."

2. Rhythm and Melody of the Music. The rhythm and melody of the music should match as nearly as possible the natural rhythmic flow of the words and the characteristic movements suggested by them. The song just cited, "Hoppy, the Kangaroo," is a good example of matching rhythm and melody in words and tune. Or take "Flip Flop," page 75, and consider three different ways in which the first phrase could be notated rhythmically and melodically:

1.
With a flip - flop here, And a flip - flop there,

2.
With a flip - flop here, And a flip - flop there,

3.
With a flip - flop here, And a flip - flop there,

Number 1 sounds tired and listless when sung. Number 2 is too wooden to describe the freedom of the fish in the cool waters of the brook. Number 3 sounds free and gay, suggesting or imitating the quick movements of the fish as it darts about. So Number 3 is decidedly the best and is therefore used in this song.

3. Mood. Everything about a song should establish and express the mood of the text. "Bright Star" on page 39, for instance, has a light and twinkling melody; and if triangles are used, as suggested, the words are even further re-enforced by the music, and the mood is thus enhanced. When the piano, accompanied by wood blocks, plays "Galloping" on page 35, it is almost impossible to refrain from galloping, so closely are the music and text allied in mood. The happiness of Christmas, the reverence felt in prayer, the gaiety of nonsense songs, the delight in pet animals, the spookiness of Halloween—all the varying moods of the child spirit can thus be reflected in both music and text.

4. Tone Quality. Although children are strongly influenced by the teacher's voice quality, they tend to imitate the *manner* of her singing to a greater extent than her exact tone quality. So it is wise for you to sing in a voice that resembles your speaking voice in quality, for this is what children expect your singing voice to be like. They are more startled than pleased to hear a person speak to them in a low-range voice and then sing in a high, unnatural tone.

A singing voice that is not used, or used infrequently, will lose some of the tones at both ends of its range—high tones and low tones. You can prevent this from happening to you by singing for a few moments daily in the upper and lower parts of your voice register. If you have already lost some tones, you can regain them by the same practice.

In spite of its importance, do not be overanxious about the tone quality of your children, for too much concern will result in tension throughout the room, killing all interest in music. But if you feel that your ear is not sensitive enough to detect poor tone quality, ask for help from someone else. And remember that many teachers who do not sing at all well are capable of getting beautiful quality from the children. Sometimes recordings are a great help with this problem.

As has been pointed out, a child may be led to develop appropriate musical expression through his concept of the mood and the imagery of the text and melody. The song should by its very nature, then, suggest an appropriate tone quality, or "color." Although the children at first imitate the tone and manner of the teacher's presentation of a particular song, they can be guided to go beyond mere imitation. If they are helped in their own expressive interpretation of a song and if they learn that there are various possibilities in song interpretation, they will have been provided with a firm foundation for musical growth.

5. Creative Implications. Beautiful singing quality is more than a particular degree of loudness or softness. It is the result of musical understanding and freedom in handling song material. Nothing that has been said above, nor anything that follows, will be truly effective if the teacher is not creative. One of her finest tools is the art of adroit questioning. Appropriate questioning is the only procedure that will insure the child's contribution in any situation. The alternative is *telling* him *what* to do and *how* and *when,* a procedure which is undesirable and stifling. This statement, however, does not mean that the child's word is the law or the last word in the classroom. It means that there should be at all times an atmosphere which will assure him that his ideas and suggestions are welcome and worthy of consideration. What the teacher then does or leads the class to do about his suggestions measures her worth and capacity to work with children.

In dealing with good songs for young children, such appropriate questioning opens up many avenues to creative activity on the part of the children. They may decide, or be led to decide, to make up a "dance" to a song, or to play the song on rhythm instruments, or to make up some more stanzas for it. They may make a "drama" of it, or even create a new song somewhat like it. Consider "The Delivery Boy" on page 27 and the various activities suggested for the song. The children, encouraged by a creative teacher, may decide to make a little "drama" of it, with the delivery boy singing (or knocking) the "knock, knock" phrases and the rest of the class singing the other phrases. They may decide to add verses and to sing "Some ice cream and some cake," even though the line does not rhyme, or "Some oranges and meat," or whatever they happen to fancy, on the final phrase as a "new" verse. Such creative activities give them a sense of musical achievement.

Uncertain, or inaccurate, singers

In any average kindergarten class, most of the children begin the school year without having learned, or having wanted to learn, to sing a melody correctly from beginning to end. This situation is no cause for alarm. Kindergarten teachers understand and expect such things. They know they must not leave the child where they find him, but they also know that this sort of thing is happening to him in all areas. In looking at a picture, in repeating a story he has heard, or in drawing an object, he tends to pick out the features which interest him most. He does not notice all the details at once—only those features that catch his attention. He needs to see a picture or to hear a melody again and again before he can take in all of the details. In the case of melody, he needs help to realize the up-and-downness, the highs and lows. He needs help

to realize that melodies have direction and shape. He needs encouragement and praise in his efforts to sing. Sometimes his effort is "not quite high enough," sometimes he is singing a "little bit low." Sometimes you can help by showing with your hand in the air the "shape" of the melody. All these efforts on your part are valuable and may save much time later on. Usually the child wants to please. Therefore, to let him sense that his musical effort is not quite right without giving him some definite idea of where and how he went wrong is to frustrate any attempt on his part to do better.

As far as singing is concerned, kindergarten children usually fall into one of these categories:

1. *The child who comes from a home where there is music and where some effort has been made to help him learn melodies.* This child has already developed a sense of pitch discrimination. He is ready for a larger repertoire of music activities. Be careful that you do not lose his interest, no matter how cooperative he may *seem* to be! Make him realize that he is learning musically, learning to make up a dance or a song, learning songs that are of different kinds (quiet, happy, sad, story, and the like). Don't let him lose sight of the fact that he *is* growing musically while he is waiting, until they catch up with him, for the children who came to school unable to sing.

2. *The child who chants or repeats the words of a song as though it were just a poem, with some attention now and then to ups and downs in his speaking voice.* First of all, he is singing in a sense because chant is a type of song. Although he uses his speaking voice, he has some idea of stress, accent, and direction. As long as there is variety of tone in his speaking voice, there will be variety of tone in his singing voice. This child has not developed a sense of pitch discrimination nor of melodic direction. Help him to listen for pitch and melodic line in the singing of his classmates and in the singing or playing of orchestral instruments on the record player.

3. *The child who uses a singing tone but does not sing the melody correctly on pitch.* This child has a singing voice but lacks the ability to discriminate pitch and melodic line. Help him to realize that the melodic line moves upward and downward or stays in the same place, and give him plenty of time to experiment vocally with these ideas.

4. *The child with an unusually low voice*. This little boy may grow up to be an excellent bass, and this little girl may become an excellent contralto, if they are not made to feel during their early school music experiences that something is wrong with their voices. Usually they begin to sing the melody correctly one octave lower than the other children, sometimes in the latter half of the first year and sometimes not until the third or fourth year of school. Help them to understand that their effort is acceptable and pleasing to you. If you accept their singing voices, the other children will accept them too. Don't worry that low singers will spoil your programs; don't let your programs spoil their enjoyment of music and perhaps kill their interest in musical development.

To aid the uncertain, or inaccurate, singers in your group, try to have many devices at hand because all children do not respond to the same one.

1. Some children find it easier to learn one short phrase of a song, or a few tones, than to match a single tone (see Song fragments following this section).

2. Others are helped by being asked to match a sustained tone on a vowel sound. If this device is used, the child should be allowed to hear the tone for a few seconds before responding.

3. Sometimes "catchy" tunes with definite ups and downs are easier for the child to sing than songs containing not much variety.

4. "Echo" games, tone calls, and the like help some children more than do any other devices.

5. The use of the piano, bells, and other melody instruments helps most with some children.

Helping the child "find" his singing voice would be a relatively simple matter were it not for the fact that we must constantly be concerned about a more important aspect of the situation, namely, the psychological effect on the child. There are many ways of helping him to understand his problem—and to know that we are all trying to help him—without having him feel that he is being set apart or left out. With this idea in mind, it is suggested that these children be not seated separately but, instead, that each one be surrounded with accurate singers. When it is necessary for them to listen, some of the better singers may be asked to listen too, so that the inaccurate singers are not in the position of being segregated as a group. Many occasions can be utilized or contrived for them to hear the song as it should sound.

Song fragments

One - tone Calls

Wake Me, page 14

The Delivery Boy, page 27

Choo Choo! page 30

Wind the Bobbin, page 55

Pease Porridge, page 81

Shoo, Fly! page 81

Looby Loo, page 83

141

Goblin in the Dark, page 113

Gob - lin in the dark!

Christmas Day, page 118

Christ - mas Day

Old MacDonald's Farm, page 128

Here a chick, there a chick

Two - tone Calls

Together, page 2

To - geth - er, to - geth - er,

Six Little Apples, page 3

Down came three

Counting Song, page 7

One, two, a cow says, "Moo!"

Knock at the Door, page 11

Knock at the door! Peep in!

What Time Is It? page 15

What time can it be? What time can it be?

Telephone, page 16

Tel - e - phone! Tel - e - phone!

Lady, Lady! page 18

La - dy, La - dy!

Listen to the Rain! page 38

Lis - ten! Lis - ten!

The North Wind's Song, page 42

Ooo ____ Ooo ____

Three - tone Calls

Building Blocks, page 4

Build - ing blocks, Build - ing blocks,

Dial the Number, page 16

This is he!

My Tree House, page 20

High in a tree, High in a tree;

Fire-Truck Song, page 24

Where is the fire? Where is the fire?
Here is the fire! Here is the fire!

Leaves, page 42

Leaves are fall - ing light - ly
Red and brown and yel - low

Jim-along, Josie, page 54

Hey, Jim - a - long,

Hoppy, the Kangaroo, page 59

Hop - sky hop! Hop - sky boo!

Pease Porridge, page 81

Nine days old.

Green Gravel, page 90

Green grav - el, green grav - el,

Happy Birthday, page 110

Hap - py Birth - day!

How to present a song to the children

There are many ways of presenting a song to the children. Therefore, vary your approach to suit the particular song being presented. After you have familiarized yourself with the song and feel the mood, use any of the four methods into which the teaching procedure usually falls:

1. Phrasewise method
2. Whole-song method
3. A combination of (1) and (2)
4. Teaching songs from recordings.

With any of these methods, the piano or the autoharp aids greatly in motivation. Most teachers prefer to use methods (2) and (3) because they believe that these provide a truly musical experience for the children and contribute to an "appreciation" of the song itself. For some songs, however, the phrasewise method is still the most satisfactory.

1. Phrasewise Method. In this procedure, the teacher sings the song for the children and then briefly tells them what it is about. She sings it a second time, asking the class to listen especially for some certain feature—perhaps the way the melody goes up and down, showing them the movement with her hand as she sings. The children thus use both ears and eyes in this teaching step. Next she presents the song one phrase at a time, asking the children to repeat each phrase after her. She then sings two phrases at a time, and so on. If the children encounter difficulty in any of the phrases, the teacher deals with it separately before she asks the children to sing the entire song. If a piano is available, the accompaniment to the song should be played sometime during the procedure outlined above. It is also helpful to hear a recording of the song at the beginning and again at the end of the lesson.

2. Whole-song Method. In this procedure, the teacher makes no phrasewise divisions of the song. It is therefore necessary for her to sing the song several times, so that the children get a good idea of it. They may respond with rhythmic movement, dancing, playing rhythm instruments, and other appropriate activities in order to make the rehearings meaningful rather than monotonous. The teacher uses her best judgment as to when the class, or a small group, is ready to try singing the entire song.

143

3. Combination of Phrasewise and Whole-song Methods.

This procedure is a compromise, and for certain types of songs a happy one. It is in essence the whole-song method with the addition of stress on certain phrases which the children can readily sing. These phrases are brought in early in the procedure, thus obviating any long delay in actual singing by the children. As an illustration, consider again "Lady, Lady!" on page 18. This song is most interestingly presented if the triangle, bells, and piano are introduced *as* the song is taught. They are a part of *learning* the song and should not be left to be added later. The teacher sings the entire song and then calls attention to the easiest phrase in it, "Lady, Lady." She asks the children to sing it while someone plays it on an instrument. Then she puts the song together again (whole song) and sings it for the class, asking them to join her on the "Lady, Lady" part. This step may be repeated a time or two, with different children handling the instruments. These teaching steps may be enough for the song on one day, and the teacher should be careful not to spend too much time on any one song at any one lesson.

When work on the song is resumed on another day, the children may be asked to add the phrase "Buy a broom for your baby" because it is easy to sing. If this goes well, the class will now be helping the teacher sing two thirds of the song. After several such repetitions, the children will have heard the whole song and participated in singing parts of it enough times for them to join in the entire song.

4. Teaching Songs from Recordings.

Children learn songs very rapidly from recordings, but a definite technique is required in teaching with the aid of the record player. The whole-song method is used, unless the teacher prefers to teach the song phrase by phrase, using her own voice, after the recording has been played once or twice. This is a good way to teach, for it gives the children the advantage of hearing the song first with instrumental accompaniment, sound effects, and the like, and then learning it phrasewise. It is desirable to finish the lesson with a rehearing of the recording. Occasionally, a nonsinging teacher relies entirely upon the recording for the actual singing.

It is difficult for small children to keep up with the recording when they attempt to sing with it. They should therefore have the opportunity of hearing it several times without singing along, but reacting to it rhythmically in order to feel the exact tempo of the song. In songs such as "Palomino," page 34, the opportunity is especially fortunate because of the implied rhythmic activities in the words or the activities in the suggestions to the teacher.

Sometimes there is confusion about the words because the voice on the record is new and strange in the classroom. After a few hearings and a little discussion as to what the song is all about, the teacher may want to teach the words separately, phrase by phrase.

Recordings must never be looked upon as a substitute teacher. They can only present the recorded versions of songs, leaving the *teaching* to be done by the classroom teacher.

Some fundamentals of music for young children

The kindergarten is, of course, the place for musical activities and experiences suitable for small children—not a place for the use of specialized musical terminology. The following *concepts* of music fundamentals, however, are such that even a very young child can learn to recognize them and be able to express them in his own singing and playing, although he does not hear the professional terminology until he is more mature.

1. Loud and Soft. Variations in tonal volume, or *dynamics,* the term used by musicians, indicates the varying degrees of loudness or softness in a composition. Through dynamics, the musician is able to make a piece of music more expressive. For the child, it is important that he experience and explore the possibilities of dynamic variety in many songs *for himself* and be not always limited to superimposed adult ideas. He naturally does not hear the term *dynamics,* but he experiences its effects. If, for instance, he is given the opportunity to sing "The North Wind's Song," page 42, in all the following ways:

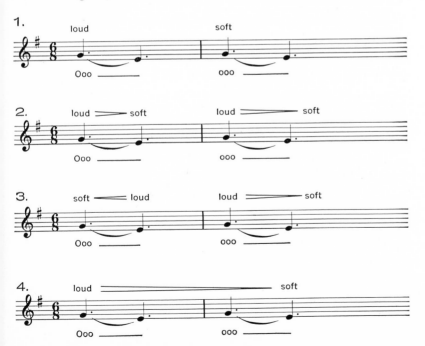

he will be learning to use dynamics to express what he feels about the sound of the north wind. Neither the teacher nor the child should feel that there is only one correct way to interpret this song dynamically, nor is there any need to ask the children which way is best. The importance lies in letting the children take part creatively in making the song say something and mean something.

A simple way of developing dynamic possibilities in a song is to teach the children to use the device of opening and closing the hands as a means of indicating louder or softer tones. Palms placed together mean "sing softly"; as the hands are opened, the tone gradually becomes louder; as the hands begin to close again, the tone becomes softer.

Instead of contrast, sustained volume of tone is sometimes very effective in expressing the musical content of a song. There should be opportunities for young children to explore the extremes of dynamic range, sometimes singing or playing very softly and sometimes very loudly throughout a song. Singing every song at the same degree of half-loudness or half-softness should be avoided because it can become monotonous and rob music of life and variety.

2. Accent. The tones of a melody usually are grouped in two's, three's, or four's, depending upon the meter signature. The slightly greater stress placed upon the accented note in singing or playing makes these groupings stand out a little more clearly. Sometimes especially expressive words call for a heavier accent, as in "An-*co*-na chick-en, *dressed* so fine," page 69. Accent adds sparkle to a line of melody because it gives life to the rhythm of the song.

A childlike way to experience and understand accent is to chant: *loud* soft soft/ *loud* soft soft/ etc., or *loud* soft/ *loud* soft/ etc. Such chants can also be expressed very effectively with rhythm instruments and bodily movement. But they must not be allowed to become wooden and meaningless and thus defeat their purpose.

145

3. High and Low. To the adult, this tonal concept seems too obvious to bother about. But all small children do not readily grasp the idea of "high" and "low" in tones. They must experience it again and again in their songs and get a visual as well as an aural concept before it becomes familiar to them. The visual concept may be provided by

(a) the teacher's hand in the air.
(b) marks or pictures on the chalk board without a music staff.
(c) figures on the flannel board without a music staff.
(d) a space-frame instrument such as bells or the piano.

The aural concept may be provided by such songs as:

page 1 Music Gets Inside Me "Mu-sic gets" in the third phrase
  low low high

page 3 Six Little Apples   first word is high, last word is low
page 37 Bumbershoot   "Push up" "Hold up"
  low high   low high

4. Melodic Direction. This adult term describes the shape and the curve of the melody with its highs, lows, ups, and downs, first detected by ear and then noticed in some visual form. The earliest representation for the children is usually the teacher's hand showing the melodic line in the air. At another time she might indicate the shape of the melody on the chalk board without a music staff, or on the flannel board using cut-out figures instead of notes on a staff.

During these early experiences, the child needs to feel the difference between the shape of "Thunder," page 39:

and the sweep of the melodic line in "A Fish Story," page 8:

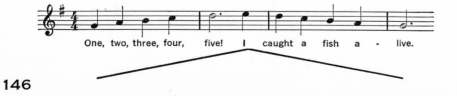

Here are other examples of the melodic line which can be made graphic in one way or another for the children:

While singing "The Family," page 11, some member of the class may play on the bells: high down down down down down down low, and repeat it for the second half of the song.

The first two phrases of "Sailing," page 32, may be pictured with cut-out sailboats on the flannel board:

The first two phrases of "A Tree Grows Straight," page 41, may be pictured with cut-out trees:

5. Fast and Slow. Directions for fast and slow are given in connection with many songs in this book and apply to singing, dramatizing, the use of rhythm instruments, and bodily movement. When bodily movement is concerned, it is a good idea to allow the child to set his own tempo for an activity. Sometimes the tempo chosen by an adult is not comfortable for him. A tempo that is too slow for skipping, for instance, may require a greater sense of balance and coordination than the child has developed so far. Here is yet another area in which he should be encouraged to "explore."

6. Phrasing, and a Feeling for the Phrase. Defining the phrase in music for the child is of no importance whatever. The important thing is that he be given many opportunities to *feel* and *react* to what we call the phrasing of a song, or its phrasewise structure. It is a matter of duration in time, not measured by the hands of a clock but by our own inner feeling or muscular timing.

The phrasing is clearly marked on the songs in this book. See, for instance, "Together," page 2, and "A Fish Story," page 8. A singer separates phrases by taking a breath. In order to develop this habit in children, many teachers use such devices as the following:

Rainbows. The teacher describes in the air a rainbow for each phrase of the song, directing the children to take a breath "when we all get over here" (the end of the arch).

Raising Hand. The teacher moves her hand from a low position to a high position on each phrase, saying, "We will take a breath when we all get to the top."

Dramatization. Because of their word content, many songs lend themselves to phrasewise dramatization, with the children *doing* what the words of that phrase suggest. If each phrase is assigned to an individual or to a group of children, a very definite and exact feeling for the phrase can be developed. Such songs as "Stand Up and Look," page 53, and "Teddy Bear," page 65, are easily dramatized phrasewise.

There is another feature of phrasing that is very important musically. It has to do with the dynamics *within* the phrase. For instance, consider the first two phrases of "Ancona Chicken," page 69:

As the melody line rises and falls, the degree of loudness or softness of tone may also rise and fall to give greater color and life to the melody.

7. Form. Just as the child can be pleased by the visual shape and tactile feel of objects (a toy airplane, the feel of balance in a hammer, the flowing lines of a streamlined train), so he can feel pleasure in being aware of the shape and balance of a song. As an example, again consider "A Fish Story," page 8. After hearing or singing this portion of the song with its upward swing:

there is a satisfaction, a feeling of completion about the downward line of the next portion that a child can be led to hear:

The complete phrase has a satisfactory melodic line because it has balance:

Repetition furnishes another kind of satisfaction in the balance and form of melodic line. There is satisfaction in the repetition of the first melody, and every good song, no matter how short, contains this characteristic to some degree:

The contrast in the third and fourth phrases is welcome. The melody seems to turn around and go in a different direction, just for a change. The return to the first melody, to finish the song, gives it a fine balance:

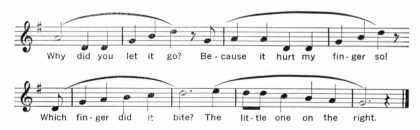

Most songs for children have one or two phrases repeated somewhere within the song, while another phrase or two furnish contrast either melodically or rhythmically. Repetition gives the song *unity*; variation gives it *contrast*. Both are present in a good melody.

Developing an Understanding of Rhythm

The ability to dance or sing rhythmically implies much more than mere movement or a sense of movement; it implies an ability to *control* movement. There is almost never a lack of responsive movement in a kindergarten, but at the very beginning of the school year the class usually shows a lack of ability to control movement. One of the first things the child must learn is how to use his body effectively: how to use his large and small muscles, his fingers, hands, and legs to give the desired response.

At this age level there are varying degrees of ability in rhythmic responses, and the children usually fall into these categories:

1. *The child who can imitate any simple rhythmic pattern.* This child can sing, dance, or play the rhythmic beat of a song alone as well as with the group. Sometimes he can add the rhythmic pattern of the words. Sometimes he can improvise a pattern while another child plays the underlying beat. This is the type of rhythmic response which is desirable for all children.

2. *The child who can sing, dance, or play rhythmically with the group but not by himself.* He is on his way to controlling his rhythmic responses but needs many chances to experiment with rhythm —with the large group, with a smaller group, and by himself. He needs to realize the responsibility of keeping a steady pattern.

3. *The child who seems to lack any sense of rhythm and coordination skills.* He is usually just a bit ahead of or behind the group rhythmically. He does not clap, chant, move, or sing exactly with them. He needs to be helped in recognizing the fact that there is a *pattern* to which the group is clapping, chanting, moving, or singing. Patience on the part of the teacher and plenty of opportunities to hear and feel what is going on rhythmically are essential for him.

Here are a few devices which prove helpful in getting the child to realize the idea of keeping to the rhythmic beat:

Play a fast pattern on sticks, asking him to match it.

Play a slow pattern on sticks, asking him to match it.

In case he cannot match either one, change your tempo to *his*, getting him to see that *the idea is to keep together*.

Ask him to sing a whole song while the class whispers the words in correct rhythm. Try to get him to keep with them in this attempt.

Take rhythm patterns from songs and ask him to match them on an instrument. Be sure that the songs you sing are familiar to the class. For instance, from "The School Bus," page 3, take:

Oh, the driv - er blows the school - bus horn.

Do not show these lines of varying length to the child; they mean nothing to him. They are used here for your convenience. The child is to listen and to make a muscular response to the pattern—to what he hears.

Ask the child to skip, and pick up his tempo on a tambourine. Tell him, "This is what I heard your shoes say," and ask him *if* he can play it. In this, as in many other instances, we have come to rely on rhythm instruments, but we must see to it that they do not become just "gimmicks" of our gadget age. We must constantly evaluate what these instruments are doing for the child. If they are used with intelligence and discrimination, they are valuable teaching tools.

Group Experiences in Rhythm with Songs

In this book, the songs provide a wealth of material for group rhythmic activities. It is somehow more satisfying to sing or clap or play together in a group than alone, but the goal to have in mind for the children is the ability to sing, dance, and play correctly in rhythm alone. The classroom must therefore provide much group experience, some discussion about what is going on, and also individual clapping, dancing, and playing to the song. Many valuable suggestions having to do with this area of rhythmic training are given in this book. For a few examples, see the following songs:

page 1 Music Gets Inside Me	page 33 Tugboats
page 7 Counting Song	page 48 Step and Clap
page 8 A Fish Story	page 50 My Fiddle
page 10-12 Finger Play Songs	page 52 When We March
page 27 The Delivery Boy	page 54 Jim-along, Josie

The child needs help in realizing the nature of rhythmic patterns and rhythmic response. He needs to be *told* about rhythms— without technicalities, of course. He needs to learn to use and understand expressions such as "beat," "Move with the music," "fast," "slow," "galloping rhythm," "lazy rhythm," and the like. He needs verbal and visual help in expressing these rhythms. As we have said, usually he wants to please, and he can sense any displeasure or irritation on the part of the teacher. He wants to know how to do things correctly, and so, if his efforts are not rhythmically acceptable, he should be helped without fuss or annoyance to see how and where he may improve.

A young child is too egocentric to enjoy any dance activity as formal as a square dance or a minuet. He may manage to go through the steps of a formal dance with much training and rehearsal, but the end result is hardly worth the time and effort needed to perfect it. In fact, such a procedure is likely to be harmful to him. It is one of those things in which adults are in danger of exploiting the young child for the purpose of entertainment. He is so "cute" as he goes through these well-rehearsed steps! But such an entertainment cannot help being a teacher-directed, teacher-centered activity in which the children usually move through dance figures without understanding or pleasure. Valuable time is consumed in forcing them to master the intricacies of some folk dance completely unsuited to their age level and interests. They will learn figure dancing easily and quickly later on in higher grades, where these dances are more appropriate for their motor and social development.

Most dances suitable for young children are combinations of natural movements—walk, run, skip, hop, and the like—and variations of them. Such natural movements, combinations of them, and variations should be experienced to the fullest in the kindergarten.

Walking. A good natural walking movement is easy and swinging, with body erect and head held high. But there are many possible variations for this movement. Through questioning the children and providing different kinds of music or percussive accompaniment or verbal chants, different *kinds* of walking are possible. Creative movement has its simple beginnings in this sort of activity.

The same kind of variations can be worked out for the following natural movements:

Running: light, heavy, fast, slow.

Tiptoeing: different levels, different speeds, with or without arm movements, in different directions, and the like.

Jumping: light and springy, heavy, in place, traveling.

Hopping: on one leg, on two legs, cross-legged, high, low, and the like.

Galloping, skipping, sliding, bending, stretching, swinging and swaying, turning, and twisting—variations in all these movements should often involve different levels: low, medium, high, sometimes indicated by the range in the musical selection. The piano pieces on pages 95-109 and many of the songs in this book carry suggestions for the free movements discussed here.

Creativity with Music Materials

Young children have naturally a creative approach to living which they should be encouraged to maintain in their attitude toward song, dance, recordings, instruments — in fact, toward everything they encounter in their school experience. Not all creative work is worth preserving; the *doing* of it is the important thing.

1. Creative Dance, or The Dance Story. Creative dance is a form of movement to music centered around the child's undirected attempt to re-create a mood, a feeling, or a story through his reaction to descriptive music. There is musical and psychological value in this type of activity because it provides the child with yet another means of expression and communication. Little equipment is needed. Some good recordings or improvised accompaniments for rhythm instruments played by a few children plus some imaginative ideas from the class are sufficient to provide a satisfactory experience.

Creative dance activities in the kindergarten can spring from many sources. Children love to retell a story, and re-creating a favorite tale in dance is a pleasure for them and a good musical experience. There are no lines to be learned in a dance story because everything is easily pantomimed. There is a discriminative value in finding just the right music for the story they choose to dance. There is a growth in poise, in grace, and in confidence from a dance attempt to formulate expressions in pantomime that makes creative dance experiments extremely worth while. Even if the dance takes no longer than a minute, even if it looks very sketchy to adult eyes, the experience can be a joy to the children.

Lack of space need not limit opportunities for creative dance. For example, it is possible for seated children to use heads, shoulders, arms, and hands in swaying, bending movements as, for instance, in portraying how a fish swims or a butterfly emerges from its cocoon. Gladys Andrews's excellent book, *Creative Rhythmic Movement for Children* (Prentice-Hall, 1954), contains valuable help for the teacher who wishes to provide her children with an extended program in this area of creative dance.

2. The Activity Song. Specialists in the dance agree that the important feature of dance for the young child is free movement to music rather than a patterned, rigid motor response. There are many types of music activities that satisfy the need of the child for movement to music which cannot be called creative dance but which nevertheless allow for some measure of creative interpretation. Four of the most important types of these activity songs are the following:

Purely directional song. This type is exemplified in "Stand Up and Look," page 53, and "Step and Clap," page 48. In each case, the text consists of directions for the movements which accompany the song. The same movements are performed by all of the children at the same moment. There is a point short of rigidity where children need to learn to do a particular thing at a particular time in company with everyone else. Songs of this type appeal to children because there is fun in all standing up together and all sitting down together, and at the same time the songs perhaps teach the child something of value that is extra-musical.

"Pretending" song. A young child can find great satisfaction in pretending to be a sailboat or a train, a donkey or a turtle, a steamroller or a jet plane. Songs that allow him to pretend and imitate can also help him experience much that will be of value to him musically: heavy and light musical accents, fast and slow tempos, and regular and irregular phrases. "Choo Choo," page 30, and "The Giraffe," page 64, are examples of "pretending" songs.

Game song. "Simon Says," page 51, and "All Around the Maypole," page 88, are game songs that allow, within the framework prescribed by the text, room for individual creative movement by the child. The moment for movement is fixed and indicated, but the movement itself is left to the child's imagination.

Dance song. This type of activity song includes those simple dances in which the movement is confined to a circle moving around with no exact pattern of steps to follow other than the general direction of a walk, a skip, a jump, and the like. They are within the scope of young children's abilities. "Let Us Dance Together," page 49, and "Jim-along, Josie," page 54, are typical examples.

All such activities as those described above contribute to the child's musical development, a better feeling for rhythm, improved muscular coordination, and a stronger feeling for form and balance in music.

3. Other Creative Activities. When a child creates a song, a dance, or a picture, he makes something of his very own, a highly personal statement. His effort is spontaneous and represents his way of dealing with the world as he finds it.

An abundance of creative work in the classroom is a sign that there is a pleasant, happy, relaxed atmosphere wherein children feel free to express themselves. If a child feels free enough to offer a comment in speech, song, or dance, let us accept his offering in the spirit in which it was made. He does not offer it for criticism, he simply regards his creativeness as something he can do. He does not criticize his effort when it is made, nor does he ponder long over the making of it. He simply shares his comment with us, and we should therefore not correct it nor prolong it in any way that will make him sorry he made it. Let us not forget that there is more than one way to stifle a child's creative impulse. We must avoid overpraise and be pleased rather than wildly enthusiastic about his contributions. There is a need for germinal ideas, but forcing creative work on the child, or taking it apart with too much criticism, brings very poor results and will eventually deprive the child of his best means of communication. There will be a great deal about him that we will never know if his creative impulse is not freely at work.

Here is an example of a truly creative effort followed by informal class comment, with the teacher remaining in the background.

This "song" was offered by Walter one morning during the music period. The tune was a repetition of three or four tones not unlike the chant of certain primitive tribes we find in the world today. It was "sung" with much dramatic emphasis and satisfaction, and it completely fascinated the class:

> Yesterday on the bus
> A big boy found a rock in the aisle
> And picked it up;
> Then he sat down
> And held it in his hand
> And didn't say anything.
> When I got off the bus
> He was still holding it.

When he had finished, a girl commented: "I don't think he would throw it." A boy said: "I would have been afraid to tell the driver because he might throw it at me." Someone else said: "I don't think the big boy would have thrown it at Walter." Various other comments made by the class revealed that the situation was perfectly clear to them. Walter had been afraid that the boy might throw the stone at someone, perhaps at him, and had been afraid to tell the bus driver. The comments were made in a comforting spirit. Walter took no part in the discussion but seemed relieved and happy when the problem was shared with the rest of the class. The children came to no decision but through discussion showed Walter that they understood and sympathized with his problem.

All this, of course, is extra-musical. Walter, really troubled by something, found a "song" the best means of expressing his worry and of asking for sympathy and understanding. His "song" had all the drama of an operatic aria for the class and was a source of satisfaction to Walter himself.

Sometimes the germinal idea for a creative activity may be arrived at through questioning. For example, the teacher may ask, "Who can sing a song about something he sees in the room? We'll try to guess where it is." Too often creativity is stifled by asking a child to make up a song about a specific object—a cat, for instance.

If the child is given more latitude and if the whole thing is a game, he is more likely to respond without hesitation.

A device used successfully by many teachers is based upon nursery rhymes. The teacher sings a melody for the first line and asks a child to respond with the second, and so on. Another helpful device is to sing a question and ask the child to sing his answer. Examples are: "How will you dress on Halloween?" "What do you want for Christmas?" "What kind of fruit do you like best?"

Creativity, of course, involves many things other than melody making. For examples, see the suggestions accompanying the following songs:

One other phase of creativity deserves attention here. It is the song story made up entirely by the children. Any number of children may contribute to the "story" because it is usually a series of short sentence songs strung together without rhyme and often without the kind of regular rhythm pattern we are accustomed to hear in composed songs. Some of the children may prefer to furnish sound effects or dances for the story. Here, again, the teacher may have to help with the germinal idea by making a suggestion or two to get things started.

All of the foregoing discussion deals with the music education of the children—with the goals to be desired, the methods to use in reaching them, and the satisfaction to be derived by both teacher and children in accomplishment. Now let us turn to a final discussion which applies to the teacher alone. There are a few suggestions and summations of techniques which may prove helpful to you, and they are offered here as an aid.

A Few Technical Hints

1. How to Locate *Do* in the Songs. The sharp farthest to the right in the key signature is called *ti*. Count up one step *(ti, do)*:

The flat farthest to the right is called *fa*. Count down to *do*:

An easy rule to remember is: In keys with more than one flat, the next-to-last flat is *do*.

2. The Autoharp. Autoharp chords have been notated in this book for the 12-bar harp. Slight departures from the harmonies in the piano score have been necessary to conform with the limitations of this instrument. The 12-bar harp is best suited to songs written in the keys of C, G, and F. But inasmuch as the songs in this book are in a great variety of keys, here is a list showing additional songs which may easily be transposed to the keys suitable for the harp.

In case you have a 15-bar autoharp, you will have three additional chords: diminished chords on C, C sharp, and D.

Here are the songs which, when transposed, may be played with autoharp accompaniment:

Page		Transpose to Key of:	Chords
1	Music Gets Inside Me	C	C-G₇-F
6	New Clothes	G	G-C-D₇
9	Five Little Alligators	G	G-C-D₇-A min.
10	Mother's Knives and Forks	G	G-D₇
11	The Family	C	C-G-D₇-G₇
14	Wake Me	G	G-D₇
15	What Time Is It	C	C-F-G₇
17	The Washing Machine	G	G-D₇
20	My Tree House	C	C-G₇
24	Fire-Truck Song	F	F-C₇
29	When the Train Comes Along	C	F-C-G₇
32	Sailing	G	G-C-D₇
33	Pull the Oars	G	G-D₇
33	Tugboats	D min.	D min. -G min.
35	Galloping	C	C-F-G₇
42	The North Wind's Song	D min.	D min. -G min.
46	Let's Plant a Tree	C	C-F-G₇
48	Robot	C	C-G₇-F
49	Let Us Dance Together	C	C-G₇-F
58	Long Summer Day	G	G-D₇
60	Cows in the Pasture	G	G-D₇-C
71	Little Redbird	G	G-D₇-C
73	Butterflies	C	C-G₇-D min.
90	Green Peas	C	C-G₇
92	Yankee Doodle	G	G-D₇-C
112	False Face	G	G-D₇
113	Halloween Pumpkin	G	G-D₇-C-A₇

3. Table of Keys and Key Chords. In the following table of keys, scales and chords, each major scale is indicated by a heavy bracket, and its relative minor (in the natural minor form) is indicated by a dotted-line bracket. To construct a harmonic minor scale, raise the seventh tone of the natural minor scale. (If the seventh tone of the natural minor scale is a flat, make it a natural; if it is a natural, make it a sharp.)

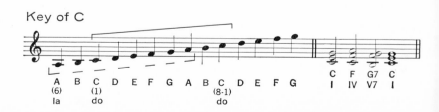

Key of G

C D E F♯ G A B C D E F♯ G
(4) (1) (8-1)
fa do do

G C D7 G
I IV V7 I

Key of D

B C♯ D E F♯ G A B C♯ D E F♯ G
(6) (1) (8-1)
la do do

D G A7 D
I IV V7 I

Key of A

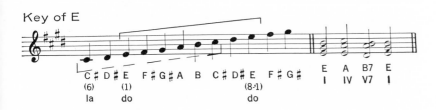

C♯ D E F♯ G♯ A B C♯ D E F♯ G♯ A
(3) (1) (8-1)
mi do do

A D E7 A
I IV V7 I

Key of E

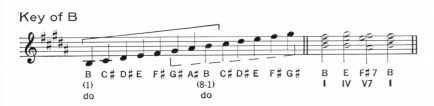

C♯ D♯ E F♯ G♯ A B C♯ D♯ E F♯ G♯
(6) (1) (8-1)
la do do

E A B7 E
I IV V7 I

Key of B

B C♯ D♯ E F♯ G♯ A♯ B C♯ D♯ E F♯ G♯
(1) (8-1)
do do

B E F♯7 B
I IV V7 I

Key of F♯

C♯ D♯ E♯ F♯ G♯ A♯ B C♯ D♯ E♯ F♯ G♯
(5) (1) (8-1)
so do do

F♯ B C♯7 F♯
I IV V7 I

Key of G♭

C♭ D♭ E♭ F G♭ A♭ B♭ C♭ D♭ E♭ F G♭
(4) (1) (8-1)
fa do do

G♭ C♭ D♭7 G♭
I IV V7 I

Key of D♭

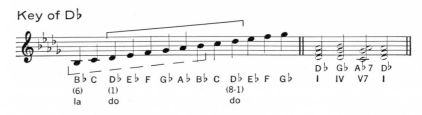

B♭ C D♭ E♭ F G♭ A♭ B♭ C D♭ E♭ F G♭
(6) (1) (8-1)
la do do

D♭ G♭ A♭7 D♭
I IV V7 I

Key of A♭

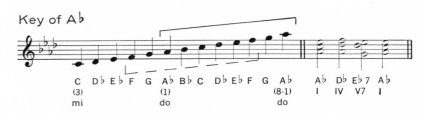

C D♭ E♭ F G A♭ B♭ C D♭ E♭ F G A♭
(3) (1) (8-1)
mi do do

A♭ D♭ E♭7 A♭
I IV V7 I

Key of E♭

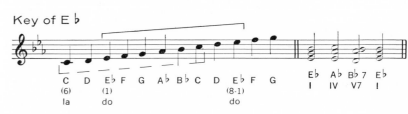

C D E♭ F G A♭ B C D E♭ F G
(6) (1) (8-1)
la do do

E♭ A♭ B♭7 E♭
I IV V7 I

Key of B♭

B♭ C D E♭ F G A B♭ C D E♭ F G
(1) (8-1)
do do

B♭ E♭ F7 B♭
I IV V7 I

Key of F

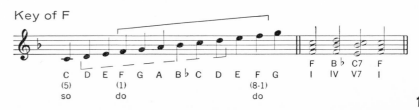

C D E F G A B♭ C D E F G
(5) (1) (8-1)
so do do

F B♭ C7 F
I IV V7 I

153

Improvisation at the Piano

Improvisation at the piano can mean many different things. It may be defined as a piano activity which is engaged in on the spur of the moment in an impromptu manner. In terms of its use in the classroom, it may be defined variously as music to highlight an activity (imitating chimes or horn effects, for instance), to illustrate a musical idea (wide skips in a song), to evoke an emotional response (sad or happy), to stimulate the imagination (sound effects for a story), and a host of other things.

For the child himself, improvisation is a form of exploration. As we know, a great deal of his early classroom experience revolves around exploration. The kindergarten and first-grade child is encouraged to experiment in painting and clay modeling. He is encouraged to use building blocks and other objects to create form and design. He should likewise be encouraged to experiment with tone at the keyboard and learn to manipulate it in the same fashion as he manipulates blocks, clay, and color in the classroom.

Improvisation is a means of acquainting the child very quickly and easily with the "up and down" of music. The singing voice may give him an aural concept, but it does not give him the visual image so important in the early phases of his learning. The keyboard furnishes him this image. Early keyboard experience helps him build the foundation for understanding the fundamentals of music —rhythm, melody, and harmony. He acquires a spatial concept of music and learns to handle the production of harmony—he has in his hand, as it were, one of the most pleasing aspects of music. He can create melodies. He can experience unusual rhythms, and, of course, explore the tonalities of major and minor modes.

A reading-readiness program for music that includes keyboard experimentation from the start is advantageous. Musical notation will almost certainly be much easier for the child if he has a basis for understanding the "whys and wherefores" of its complexities. It is logical that any early experience with the spatial relationships so evident on the keyboard will later help him to understand these same relationships on the printed page. Seeing ▦ as he sings and hears the pitch sets the stage for his later understanding of 𝄞♩♩ . He sees and feels space

between the notes, thereby developing the idea that some notes "skip" while others are "next door."

Letter names for the piano keys  are not used until the child has had an adequate orientation in music via the keyboard. In the early stages, such expressions as "the note inside the twins' house" ▦ or "the note just above the triplets' house" ▦ are easier for him to understand. As he grows in his understanding of music and the keyboard, letter names may be substituted. By the time notation is introduced, the child is well aware of such musical ideas as "direction of the melody line," "skips," and "repeated notes"—all vitalized through keyboard experience.

For the teacher, improvisation of course includes much more. Frequently, the musically inexperienced classroom teacher is unable to play the pieces in her books. She may not have the finger coordination or the musical background to play a straight accompaniment for a rhythmic activity. Or she may not have the vocal technic to insure an acceptable job of singing. Therefore a few basic ideas for creating practically any kind of music for guided rhythmic activities are outlined later in this section for her aid and convenience. It does not require a great deal of skill for her to begin this kind of improvisation, and she can later elaborate upon it or keep it as simple as the particular situation demands.

1. When Does the Classroom Teacher Need to Improvise? The classroom teacher needs to improvise when the occasion arises—on the spur of the moment. Let us say that the children have just listened to a story about wild animals or are just back from a trip to the zoo. Of course, there are songs in the book about the animals in the zoo, but these are based upon experiences that another person has had. These are not the children's own experiences. As the children re-live their recent experience and as the classroom teacher helps them improvise their own music for it, she will be able to lead them into the songs in the book, which will then become a part of their total experience.

There can be no set time to plan or call forth a creative musical activity. Sometimes the best music period comes out of a wiggly, excited, and restless group of children in the morning. They are not ready to settle down to any of the other activities. The teacher can capitalize on the rhythm of the group and their emotional feeling to work off this "steam" into a productive musical experience. Then, there are opportunities that may arise during the course of the day. The sensitive classroom teacher does not need to turn to the book to grasp the situation and to make it meaningful to the children. Rather, she has at her fingertips the means of bringing these situations to life. Also, children like to make up new songs, which often can be enlivened by additional verses and the sound of the piano, to give them a feeling of rhythm and harmony. Finally, children frequently like to put a report or story in the form of music. As they do so, the next logical step is for them to dramatize it by means of interpretive dance or physical movement accompanied by improvisation at the piano.

2. How to Improvise at the Piano.

Piano improvisation begins with what we have: the piano keyboard and our fingers. We can run our fingers to the right on the keyboard to give the effects of going high (very high in terms of the child's vocal production) or we can let our left hand sweep downward on the keyboard to explore the low registers of music.

Even as we explore "high" and "low" we may be exploring "loud" and "soft." A child will frequently come to the piano and place his hands softly on the upper keys, thereby experiencing "high" but at the same time discovering what "soft" is. He may, on the contrary, strike the piano a sharp blow and experience the piercing effect of the shrill upper register. We do not have to verbalize what is "high," what is "loud" or "soft," or the fact that "high" may be loud *and* soft. On the contrary, the child can tell us because he has experienced it.

The same applies for "fast" and "slow." To tell a little child to sing "fast notes" is useless in the early stages of musical development. He does not know what we mean. But he can *experience* "fast" and "slow," as has been pointed out earlier in this book, when he has to manipulate the large and small muscles of his body in movement. He can also experience "fast" and "slow" when he plays a series of notes in rapid sequence with his index finger or his hand. An example of this is to sing from C to G as rapidly as we wish and then to play all the notes between C and G in as rapid

sequence as possible with the index finger (or all five fingers). Which way gives the most obvious example of motion?

The concepts of high-low, loud-soft, and fast-slow can be simultaneously experienced in combination and in a great variety of ways. "Fast" may become syncopated, "loud" may go to "medium loud," "high" may be combined with "fast," and so on. The possibilities are unlimited, and the only requirement is that the teacher use her imagination to get her pupils to do the same.

Let us consider for a moment some specific illustrations of improvisation at the piano. You will notice that our terminology, "improvisation at the piano," is far more inclusive than one might think at first glance. We are considering the piano as a *resource* instrument, not as an *accompaniment* instrument. For instance, how can we use the keyboard to explore what "walking" (or stepwise) movement sounds like? We take our index finger and move stepwise up or down the keyboard. The children will immediately want to experience the effects of jumping or skipping from one note to another to get the feeling of wider intervals. Or, how can we interpret the music of rain by using the piano? The children will come to the piano and look for "raindrops." These may be random high notes, they may be two notes "plunked" together, or they may be notes from any part of the keyboard. It will not be long before one of the pupils has demonstrated the sound of thunder on the piano.

In the classroom we frequently have access to jingle bells. What sound do these bells have? One of the children might go to the piano and play a cluster of high treble notes to show that his ear has told him that the bells have a high, soft sound. How about bells that give a chime effect, such as church bells? We discover that we get a good effect by holding down the pedal and playing only the black keys:

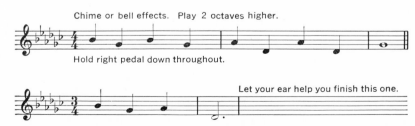

Chime or bell effects. Play 2 octaves higher.

Hold right pedal down throughout.

Let your ear help you finish this one.

We soon discover the tune to be the one Big Ben plays.

In this machine age of ours, we have many sounds around us all the time. One of the most frequent is the sound of the horn—the horn of the automobile, the bus, the diesel engine, the big ship, and the foghorn. These all have definite pitches. Let us explore them and find where they are on the keyboard.

We can also experience different moods which music portrays; for example, the soft, chordal music similar to that used for religious purposes or for quiet time. These same chords may have a completely different meaning when they are struck quite sharply. The children can readily understand what one of the functions of dynamics in music is, if these chords are given different treatments.

3. Developing an Approach to Improvisation.

What steps shall we take in developing an approach to improvisation at the piano? Our first step is to explore for ideas. Let us take the child's interest in animals. Today practically every child in our country either has seen a picture of a bear in a book or on TV or has made a trip to the zoo. Our idea might be to use the bear as a subject for musical ideas. The children may tell us that he growls, walks, or dances, or perhaps rides a unicycle. Of course, they will undoubtedly recall that bears also like to sleep. Here we have good material for improvisation and musical development.

Second, let us capitalize on daily activities, such as walking, running, skipping, dancing, whispering, and the like.

Third, children love to tell stories and let their fancies have free rein. One of their most fascinating games is telling a story without words, through musical sounds alone. A child might go to the piano and play a sequence of even notes with his index finger at a moderate tempo in the middle of the keyboard. Suddenly, with his other hand, he bursts forth with a loud cluster of tones deep in the bass. Then he resumes quickly with his right hand, playing the notes rapidly now and finally playing softer. The rest of the class would have little difficulty in supplying him with many interpretations of this story. One might be about a boy walking home from school and encountering the big dog around the corner that jumped out with a growl and scared him. He ran home as fast as he could.

The basic factors in improvisation are rhythm, mood, tempo, melody, and harmony. Improvisation may not have all of these in any one piece. For example, frequently it will have only rhythm,

tempo, and a detached or fragmentary type of melody. Of course, these set up the mood, but there is no harmony. In contrast, a child might like the sound of random tone clusters or chords, thereby having harmony but little regular rhythm, a very uncertain or almost indistinct tempo, and no melody. Again, however, we have mood.

Let us reconsider the bear story as a means of exploration for improvisation. One of the children may immediately think of the bear's growl, which he depicts by placing the palm of his hand on the lower keys of the piano (black and white). He may roll the keys from left to right, right to left, or play them by moving his hand up and down directly on them. As the bear gets up, he will undoubtedly do a little scratching. The child might attempt to depict this action by playing two fingers side by side almost simultaneously:

And, as the bear scratches, he will of course yawn and say, "Ho hum." At this time, the children will find the sound of the "Ho hum" on the piano keyboard:

The bear might growl again as he starts to walk. Then he might start to dance, again accompanied by scratches and growls, until finally he is interrupted by a drop of rain falling on his nose. Mr. Bear leaves in great haste (fast effect on the piano gradually getting softer). This story is one of many variations, and it never comes out the same way twice, since the children will, in the final analysis, have it come out the way they feel at the particular time.

4. How to Improvise for Guided Rhythmic Activities.

If you wish to improvise your own accompaniments for guided rhythmic activities such as walking, running, hopping, and the like, the following examples will help you. They contain the most common patterns for daily activities. It is important to remember that these patterns may be altered, developed, and adapted as each situation demands. Do not worry about playing a wrong note, since you can always work it into the melodic progression. If you keep going, the occasional dissonance of a "wrong" note does little more than add variety and spice to the melodic line.

Be simple in your improvisation and stay with the basic pattern until you have complete freedom in playing I, V_7, I (or I, IV, V_7, I) chord patterns. This particular pattern will enable you to harmonize literally hundreds of folk songs and will give you the basic chords for any needed type of improvisation. Do not hesitate to explore new chord patterns and seek out unusual sounds for sound effects. The main rule in improvisation is to use your imagination and keep going.

First of all, play these chord patterns:

Basic Chord Patterns
(I—V7 Chords)

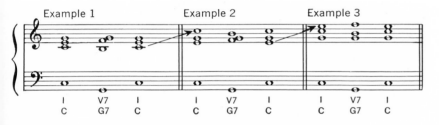

Practice these chords until their tonality is fixed in your mind. It is wise, also, to practice the chords in other keys, as they are given on pages 152-153.

You can break these chords and play the following variants:

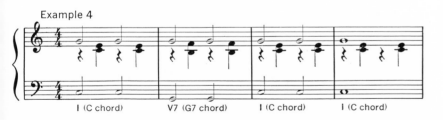

Notice that the bass note is the name-note of the chord: C in the bass for a C chord, G in the bass for the G7 chord.

Variety in the bass line can be obtained by alternating the root (name-note) and the fifth of the chord:

Here the fifth of the I chord is played an octave lower to gain a better bass line:

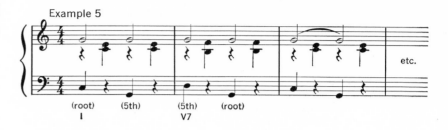

Now, by using different chord tones as the top note of the right hand, interesting melodies can be created:

This example starts with another tone of the I chord. See how many other ways you can play it beginning on the same note:

157

Here is still another possibility with which you can experiment:

Example 8

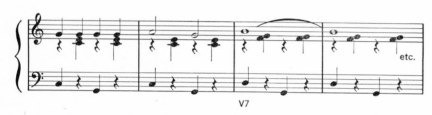

Practice the preceding chord patterns and their variants in all keys whenever you can. As soon as you get the "feel" of the chord patterns, create your own variations.

* * *

Now here are patterns using the IV chord:

Example 9   Example 10   Example 11

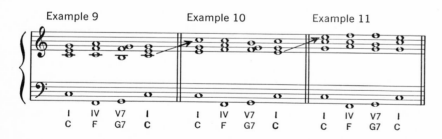

Try these chord patterns in the same manner as Examples 4-8.

* * *

The following are examples for using the I, IV, and V7 chords in creating accompaniments for classroom activities:

Walking
(I and V7 chords)

Example 12

Vary the tempo for fast and slow walking.

Walking
(I, IV, and V7 chords)

Example 13

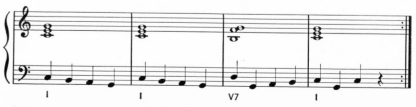

The IV chord may be used in the following examples as it is in Example 13.

Running

Example 14

Or vary it like this:

Apply these basic ideas, with which you have been experimenting, in improvising accompaniments for other classroom activities, such as

Trotting

Example 15

Skipping

Example 16

Galloping

Example 17

Sliding or Waltzing

Or vary it like this:

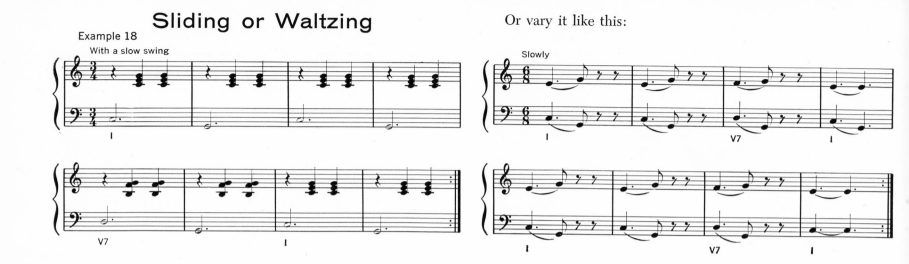

Improvisation at the piano, when properly approached, is one of the most direct ways of releasing human inhibitions. It is a real friend, and one of the finest musical aids available. Perhaps one of the most important functions of the piano in your musical experiences and those of your group is that the piano, more than any other single instrument, including the voice, provides something just for you and your class. As time goes on, you can experience more music and gain greater competency and expressiveness through improvisation. Music will give you something far above and beyond the daily classroom routine.

*　　　*　　　*

INDEXES

Alphabetical Index of Recordings

One album of two LP recordings.   Produced by Audio Education, Inc., distributed by American Book Company

Sectional Index of Recordings

INDEX OF SONGS